ARBOREAL MAN

ARBOREAL MAN

BY

F. WOOD JONES, M.B., D.Sc.

PROFESSOR OF ANATOMY IN THE UNIVERSITY OF ADELAIDE
FORMERLY PROFESSOR OF ANATOMY IN THE UNIVERSITY OF LONDON
(LONDON SCHOOL OF MEDICINE FOR WOMEN)

THIRD IMPRESSION

HAFNER PUBLISHING COMPANY
New York   London

1964

Originally published 1926
Reprint 1964

———————

Printed and published by
HAFNER PUBLISHING COMPANY, INC.
31 East 10th Street
New York, N.Y. 10003

Library of Congress card catalog number 64-21054

To
MY WIFE

PREFACE

THE subject, with which the following pages deal, formed the material for certain Arris and Gale Lectures, delivered in the Theatre of the Royal College of Surgeons of England during the years 1915 and 1916. Chapter XXI. consists of a condensed, and only partial, account of the subject treated in one such Lecture on " The Influence of the Arboreal Habit in the Evolution of the Reproductive System," delivered on March 22nd, 1915; and the remaining chapters formed the basis of three Lectures on " The Influence of the Arboreal Habit in the Evolution of Man," delivered on February 28th, March 1st, and March 3rd, 1916.

Among their literary defects are those which are inseparable from their origin, since they are at best but elaborated notes of separated headings under which the Lectures were originally planned. The gift, which was so peculiarly conspicuous a possession of Huxley, of endowing the written page with the interest felt by the lecturer in the preparation of his subject, is a rare one. For the most part, the written notes of lectures are wont to present themselves as mere disconnected assertions, woven around a series of apparently disjointed central ideas. It is this inherent difficulty of reducing the underlying thought, and the spoken word to a consecutive written statement, that is appealed to as an excuse for the partially woven condition in which the material is presented to the reader. And this excuse is urged the more insistently since an alternative one will readily present itself. The want of proper literary sequence might indicate equally well that the subject had been but insufficiently thought over, that the sequence of ideas had been ill considered, and the conclusions hastily arrived at. That in this case the matter is not so can best be urged by stating that the substance of these Lectures had been collected in the form of written notes some seven years ago. Moreover, many of the details and the ideas included in these pages I have been accustomed to incorporate in the ordinary routine teaching of Medical Students at Manchester University, at St. Thomas's Hospital, and at the London School of Medicine for Women.

I have endeavoured to acknowledge my indebtedness to the work of others wherever such a debt has been incurred. Some debts, however, cannot be considered as discharged by the mere acknowledgment of the source of a quoted passage; to Professor Arthur Keith, and to Professor G. Elliot Smith, I owe far more than is implied in the few references made directly to their written works.

The figures which are reproduced here are selected from those drawn to illustrate the Lectures; they were prepared with especial regard for their appearance when magnified by the epidiascope rather than when reduced by the processes of reproduction.

F. W. J.

LONDON,
October, 1916.

CONTENTS

ARBOREAL MAN

CHAPTER I

THE PROBLEM OF MAN'S ORIGIN

IT is a strangely difficult thing, for one of our generation, to picture the acuteness of the upheaval brought about in 1859 by the publication of the " Origin of Species." It is hard to realize that there should have been so much novelty in the ideas expressed in the book that thought should have been overwhelmed by the new teaching; that " evolution " should have become a creed; and that " special creation " should have become an obsession. So many suggestions had gone forth before, so much of the path had been paved for evolution, that it seems strange how the basal idea that species were not specially created, and definitely fixed types of life, should have suddenly, as a flame, lit up the fires of the most bitter controversy carried on in modern times.

It is the more wonderful when we think that, at any rate as far as the scientific world was concerned, Darwin was by no means standing as the pioneer of evolution; but was only the thoughtful student who was putting forward some easily understood explanation of the manner in which evolution had been effected.

And yet of the upheaval of thought that occurred we, separated by more than fifty years from the advent of that work, can feel the bitter reality when turning the pages of any contemporary periodical in the columns of which some of the many battles were waged. Even when the opening period of hasty and unreasoning partisanship was passed, and after the first skirmishes had been fought and won for the principle of evolution, there still remained the biggest battle of all to be contested. Fifty years ago even an ardent evolutionist would feel no difficulty in keeping as a mental reservation the belief that, though no doubt the lesser beasts had been subject to the laws of gradual change, Man was aloof from all this and was a divine, a special, and a perfected creation. This mental reservation is, not unnaturally, still prevalent to-day; and I think that in 1916 one would give but an ill picture of the popular progress of the ideas first made definite by the work of Darwin, if one assumed that, in the dying of controversy, there had of necessity been a really wide acceptance of the picture of a simple evolutionary origin of Man. How completely Man can be separated, by a series of mental processes, from all the laws known to govern the modifications and progress of lower animals, even by a man of the highest scientific attainments, may be realized by the reading of such a work as the final effort of Thomas Dwight, the late distinguished Professor of Anatomy of Harvard. What Dwight, possessed of a vast store of knowledge of the structure and variations of Man and the lower animals, could do, a great host of others can do in the comfortable absence of any such precise knowledge which might influence the attitude they elected to adopt.

Still, despite the mental reservations of the thinking few, and the unthinking many, the questions must be asked and answered: What are the factors of habit or environment, and what are the steps of " adaptation," " variation," or " sporting " which have led to the evolution of Man as a zoological type ?

We start, therefore, with the assumption that we accept the principle of evolution as a fact, and that we extend this principle to embrace Man. " Adaptation," " variation," and " sporting " have been named in that order of set purpose, and for a very special reason which must be briefly defined.

Change comes about somehow in animal types, that must be admitted, else there could be no groundwork for the play of evolution. Change might conceivably come about by " adaptation," and by that is meant the reaction of the animal to its life surroundings. John Hunter (1728-1793) had a clear conception of this influence, and his life work might be summed up by saying that he saw, with the eye of a genius, the dependence of structure on function. With the alteration of function —not uncommonly as a result of change of environment or habit—structure, in the individual, shows harmonious change.

As an inheritable, and so as an evolutionary, factor, this adaptation of structure to function is especially associated with the name of Jean Baptiste de Monet, Chevalier de Lamarck (1744-1829), who, quite Hunterian in his conceptions, appreciated to the full the influences of " use and disuse " upon organs and systems.

Changes, again, might be brought about, not by special, definite, and purposive " adaptations," but by slight " variations," and by " variations " we here mean those trivial congenital differences, always displayed among individuals, which are the progeny of parents possessing varied individualities.   Variation, aided by natural selection, constitutes that particular method of effecting change in living things especially associated with the name of Charles Darwin (1809-1882).   By " sporting " or "mutation " is understood, not a purposive adaptation, nor a mere gradually accumulating minor congenital variation, but the more or less sudden appearance of a " freak," if one may so express it, among the offspring of an individual. Evolution, by sporting or by mutation, is a more modern conception, associated in the main with the name of De Vries, and a host of contemporary workers.

These are ideas that are, or have been, current in

accounting for change in the living world. Change comes about in some way—that is obvious; by what channel or channels it comes about concerns the present inquiry but little. How it is transmitted once it came into being, how it is accumulated, perfected, and handed on are questions which, despite an enormous amount of work, and despite an accumulated literature of dogmatic, and sometimes unjustified assertion, are at present unknown. Without touching upon these problems it is proposed to examine the probable path by which the Primates and Man have originated, reviewing the influences that have probably reacted upon them, but leaving aside the questions as to how changes have come into being, and how such changes have been inherited. We will therefore define our position by saying that change has been effected somehow, and somehow it has been handed on; and that any attempt to chronicle the progress of these changes need not be branded as Lamarckian or impossible, as Darwinian or improbable, as mutationist or orthodox, unless definite assertions are made as to the exact mode or means by which these alterations have come into being, or have become handed on and stereotyped.

Man has often been discussed as an evolutionary product; the literature of the last fifty years teems with works upon that special aspect of anthropology which deals with Man as the highest of the Primates. There is nothing to be added to the brilliant generalizations of Huxley, nothing to be altered in the careful analysis of primate and human characters carried out by Keith. One reason only has appealed to the writer as an excuse for the publication of these lectures, and that is the fact that the paleontological history of Man is rapidly enlarging. Any new find of a so-called " missing link " may bring us by chance nearer to deciding in what type human divergence first manifested itself. Disputes concerning the zoological rank of such finds will, in all probability, be carried on with extreme vigour for many years to come. That is inevitable, and it can only result, in the end, in a gain to the scientific knowledge of the origin of Man. Meanwhile it is advisable to take stock of what is probable concerning the phylogenetic story of Man, in order to see if there is any stage in his evolution at which he, or his remains, might be labelled as human. Not so long ago there would have been no hesitation in asserting what type was, and what was not, human. Man began as Man, and that was the beginning and the end of it. We have definitely passed that stage. To-day we have a bewildering complexity of genera and species of missing links; but we still have a more or less definite conception of what we would term a human being. It has been claimed that the possession of the ability to speak constitutes an essential feature of the dawning human being, and it has even been imagined that, from a study of the fragmentary physical remains of missing links, the presence or absence of this faculty could be determined. Physical remains cannot provide the material from which certain knowledge upon this point may be gleaned. There is no more reason for saying that some such missing link could not speak because some divergence from the modern human type is found in the construction of the jaw, than there is for asserting that a monkey cannot play the piano because the anatomy of his hand differs in some details from that of a human pianist. No ape has become an orator, and no monkey a distinguished performer upon the piano; but we must not seek the reason for this in the departures from the standard human form seen in the structure of their jaws and hands. Speech, and piano-playing, are the outcomes of a series of elaborations of cerebral processes which are present in existing Man, but not in existing monkeys. We have no certain physical clue in the fragmentary remains of missing links concerning the presence or absence of these elaborations of cerebral processes.

There is a very prevalent idea that the assumption of

the upright posture in terrestrial progression gave to Man those special attributes which we would term human. There can be no possible doubt that the faculty for striding about upright upon the surface of the earth marked a very real phase in evolution. But when we come to examine the possible influences which preceded this departure, we can only regard it as a natural and culminating phase of a long series of changes which had taken place in an altogether different environment. Were the whole series of missing links to be paraded before us in the form of their fragmentary remains which are yet to be discovered, he would be a bold man who would point to any individual member as the one in which the features of terrestrial uprightness argued humanity. Arboreal uprightness preceded terrestrial uprightness; and it is the purpose of these studies to show, in some measure, the extent to which Man is indebted to, and was perfected in, arboreal life.

Man comes of an arboreal stock. Two questions arise. When in the phylogeny of the Mammals did this stock become arboreal, and when did it give rise to a creature which we could possibly term human ? The first question is capable of an approximate solution; the second is unanswerable, but we may say with regard to it that, if the term " humanoid " may be permitted, such a stock may have had a very early representation among the mammalian fauna.

CHAPTER II

THE EMANCIPATION OF THE FORE-LIMBS

WE may not here turn aside to inquire into the origin of limbs, nor pause to consider the questions which of necessity arise out of the fact that, while all Vertebrates are limited to four limbs, the Invertebrates know no such limitation.

We will start with the facts as we know them: that Vertebrates possess four outgrowths from the body segments, arranged as a symmetrical pectoral, and a symmetrical pelvic, pair of limbs; and that these limbs appear probably in their elemental form as the fins of fishes. We may assume that the most primitive type of Vertebrate limb is an appendage, which is adapted for the purpose of ordered and regulated progression. Limbs may merely propel the aquatic vertebrate body in a definite direction as oars propel a boat; and yet, even when we may regard them as a new acquisition in the Vertebrate phylum, they already subserve other functions. Some fishes propel themselves through the water by movements of their fins—they "swim"; but the source of real propulsion in a great many is the lateral movements of the tail, the fins serving far more as balancing and regulating organs than as a means of propulsion through the water. This possibility of the limbs developing a balancing function is one that becomes greatly elaborated in the story of the limbs of higher animals.

We are more immediately concerned here with the limbs of those Vertebrates higher than the fishes; and the type of limb from which we will start our comparisons

is that seen in living forms among the tailed Amphibians,
and in some of the less specialized Reptiles. This we
may define as a limb of three segments: arm, forearm,
and hand; thigh, leg, and foot (see Fig. 1). The first
segment consists of muscles massed round one central
bone—humerus or femur; the second segment of two
parallel bones—ulna and radius, or fibula and tibia, and

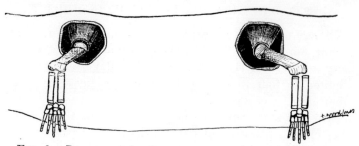

Fig. 1.—Diagrammatic Drawing to show the Condition
of Primitive Limbs.

their regulating muscles; and the third of a series of small
bones—carpals or tarsals, with the muscles and bones of
the separate digits. This limb is possessed of a high
degree of mobility. It can move in all directions on the
trunk at the shoulder and hip joints; the second segment
is enabled to move on the first by bending or straightening of the elbow or knee; the two parallel bones of the
second segment may move upon each other, so that the
third segment may be moved with the second, and be
turned (at any rate to some extent) palm or sole up
—supinated, or knuckles up—pronated (see Figs. 2, 3).
Finally the third segment is free to move on the second
in a variety of ways at the wrist and ankle. Such is the
limb which is the heritage of all land-living Vertebrates,
and such a limb is beyond doubt the heritage of the ancestral Mammal. The functions of this primitive limb
are simple in the extreme; it enables the animal to walk
about under water, and it serves to drag the animal about

on land. By its mobility it produces movement, *but it does not support the weight of the animal's body.* It is a propelling, but not a supporting, limb (see Fig. 4).   A

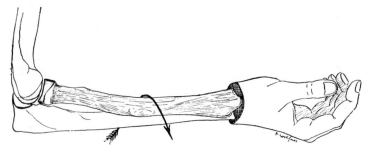

FIG. 2.—HUMAN FOREARM WITH THE HAND TURNED PALMAR
SURFACE UPWARDS—SUPINATED.

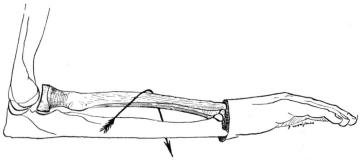

FIG. 3.—HUMAN FOREARM WITH THE HAND TURNED PALMAR
SURFACE DOWNWARDS—PRONATED.

FIG. 4.—DIAGRAMMATIC OUTLINE OF A PRIMITIVE TYPE OF
VERTEBRATE WITH PROPELLING, BUT NOT SUPPORTING,
LIMBS.

very near approximation to our ideal primitive limb is seen in the ordinary water newt. We may readily appreciate, in watching such an animal, the perfection with which its limbs enable it to walk at the bottom of its tank, to clamber over obstacles, or climb aquatic plants. But we note that when on dry land its activities are considerably hampered, since while its limbs propel it forwards they no longer carry its weight, and the body is dragged along the ground. " On thy belly shalt thou go " applies to the pioneers of the land-living Vertebrates; for their limbs are not yet adapted to supporting their bodies and carrying them sheer of the ground.

Mobility is the keynote of this primitive limb. With the permanent exchange of an aquatic for a terrestrial habitat the limbs took on a new function, for in addition to acting as mere propellers, they now serve to lift the body during the act of propulsion. With this change a new demand is made in the structure of the limb, for *stability* must be added to *mobility*. There is a gradual evolution of this new function. The limbs at first support the body only during the act of propulsion; when the movement is over, the body sinks to rest upon the ground. In the next phase the support of the body by the limbs becomes permanent; the demand for stability in the limbs is increased. There is an antagonism in this evolution between the advantage of elaborating the ancestral, and useful, mobility of the limb, and the need for the newly developed, and essential, quality of stability. It is in this antagonism of developmental needs that the great interest of the study lies.

In such a question as this the records of paleontology are likely to furnish much material assistance, and it is from the paleontologist that the most definite pronouncements may be expected. The remains of animals furnish some clear guides as to the possibility of their limbs being supporting as well as propelling organs, and the geological period at which animals possessing such limbs first appeared seems to be generally agreed on. We find in this feature, as we shall repeatedly find again in relation to other things, that the search for these animals must be pushed very far back in the geological record, and when it is so pushed back it leads to a curious group of animals known as the Therapsida, which, presenting a blend of primitive reptilian and primitive mammalian characters, flourished in the Triassic. It was, according to Broom, among the South African members of the Therapsida especially that the limbs became supporting organs, and he has said very definitely that " when the Therapsidan took to walking with its feet underneath and its body off the ground it first became possible for it to become a warm-blooded animal." The change that we have been picturing was, therefore, one which took place very far back in the geological past; and, according to Broom, the supporting limb and the mammalian possibilities made their appearance together, the one being dependent upon the other. The characters of the supporting limb as opposed to the purely propelling, but not supporting, limb are so definite that there should be but little hesitation on the part of an anatomist in assigning the proper functions to the limbs of any extinct form. But it cannot be said that the geologist, when assuming the rôle of an articulator of the skeletons of extinct monsters, has always shown a nice appreciation of these characters. A visit to the geological galleries of any museum will reveal instances of animals, the limbs of which are articulated for a function that they had no power to perform.

Looking broadly at the Mammals, we may say that the preservation and elaboration of the inherited mobility of the fore-limb is an essential for the culmination of evolution. We may also say that this preservation of mobility must start very early, before ancestral mobility had become lost in the development of stability; and that the most successful Mammals must, by some means or other, have preserved and stereotyped this mobility almost at the outset of their mammalian career. Again, we may say that two distinct lines have been followed. Some mammals have perfected the new, and mammalian, demand for stability; and others have retained a primitive mobility in, at least, the fore-limb.

It is the latter which have been successful and have become dominant. The problem we are attempting to solve is: Why have some Mammals retained this primitive feature of mobility of the fore-limb, and why have these same Mammals become more successful in the struggle of evolution ?

We are here face to face with a fundamental problem, and it is now necessary that we should, as it were, take sides. Man possesses a mobile fore-limb which takes no part in the support or the progression of his body. He is the culmination of a line of ancestors which, on altogether different grounds, is distinct enough in general outlines. The question is: Does the stock from which Man arose retain a primitive mobile fore-limb, or has he evolved his present posture and the present freedom of his fore-limb from a previously four-footed or quadrupedal ancestor ? It may be said with truth that every teaching of modern orthodox anatomy and anthropology would lead us to believe that Man had evolved from a quadrupedal pronograde mammalian stage. With that it is impossible to disagree so long as it is made perfectly clear that the stock from which Man is derived was differentiated so early in the mammalian story, that the primitive mobility of the fore-limb had never been sacrificed to the needs of stability. There are two ways of regarding this problem. We may assume that the primitive mammal passed into a regular pronograde four-footed stage with four supporting limbs, and from that stage Man evolved into an animal characterized by an orthograde or upright posture. Or we may imagine that the stock from which Man was derived had never been typically pronograde with four supporting limbs; that in this stock mobility had never become sacrificed to stability in all four limbs. It is in the former view, the assumption of the upright posture from a pronograde stage, that much of the interest of the modern study of human morphology is centred.   It is the latter view, that the human stock has never been typically prono grade and four-footed, that is here put forward as the truth.

In attempting to maintain this view, definite answers must be given to three questions.   The first: What was the factor that saved the particular mammalian stock which culminated in Man from becoming four-footed pro.iogrades?"   We will answer by saying at once, " The arboreal habit."   The second: "When did this factor come into play in the philogenetic history of the Mammals?"   We will dismiss this by asserting that it was at the very outset, at the very dawn of mammalian life.   The anatomical basis for this assertion will be given in detail later on.   The third: " How did this factor enable that particular stock to acquire supremacy?" will be answered, so far as is possible, by the study of the influence of the arboreal habit upon the animal body.

We will deal first with the influence of the arboreal habit upon the structure and function of the limbs.   We are assuming that the primitive Mammal, new born from the Therapsidian ancestor, possesses limbs such as we have defined, with but little stability, but with a high degree of mobility, and this mobility includes the power of rotating the second and third segments around the central axis of the limb in the actions of pronation and supination.   The effects of mammalian habit upon these limbs will probably be best appreciated by following the story as it is unfolded in animals that directed their newly acquired mammalian possibilities into the natural channel of supremacy in walking and running over the surface of the earth.

All four limbs of such an animal will become equally developed as organs of support and of progression (see Fig. 5).   Mobility at shoulder, elbow and wrist, hip, knee and ankle will be essential, but stability becomes a prime necessity, and the rotation of the parallel bones of the second segment is a hindrance to perfect stability. Little by little this power of rotation becomes lost; the muscles which produce the movements of pronation and supination disappear, or change their action, the joints between the two parallel bones become less perfect; finally the

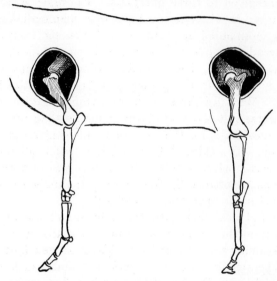

FIG. 5.—DIAGRAMMATIC DRAWING TO SHOW THE CONDITION OF LIMBS WHICH HAVE BECOME THOROUGHLY STABLE, AND FUNCTION BOTH AS PROPELLING AND SUPPORTING ORGANS.

two bones fuse together, and one member of the pair practically ceases to exist. Again, the digits, except by virtue of the nails or claws which they bear, cease to be of great individual importance, and some of them soon become reduced to the condition of mere rudiments. The final stage of this process is exemplified in the horse, where one functional digit alone remains, upon the nail (hoof) of which the animal is supported. These four limbs are now stable props which, capable of very definite and specialized movements, support the animal and

enable it to walk and run with the very greatest perfection. As a general statement, we have said that the
evolution that produces limbs of this type also demands
that all four members shall function alike, fore-limbs and
hind-limbs being both supporting and ambulatory organs.
This statement needs some qualification, since there are
certain exceptions to the rule that all four limbs are
functionally of equal importance in the Mammals that
have taken to a pronograde terrestrial life; and it is these
exceptions that are of interest. In different types of
quadrupedal Mammals there may be well-marked differences in the actual method of movement of the limbs in
ordinary leisured progression.

A right fore-limb and a left hind-limb may be raised
simultaneously from the ground and swung forwards;
this is the mode of the greater number of quadrupeds.
Again, a right fore-limb and a right hind-limb may be
raised and advanced simultaneously; this is the ordinary
mode of progression of the giraffe. Or, again, the sequence
of bringing the limbs into play may vary with the pace
at which the animal travels; and then the animal changes
its gait and its stride as the pace varies. An altogether
different method may manifest itself with this change of
gait in response to the demands of pace, and both fore-
limbs and both hind-limbs may be raised and advanced
alternately. This mode is habitual in the ordinary quiet
gait of some animals; it is the usual way in which a rabbit
moves about when feeding undisturbed. In this method
of movement the fore-limbs and the hind-limbs may play
an equal part, or the hind-limbs may take an increasing
share in the work, both of supporting the body, and of
urging it forward. In this way a more and more perfect
hop is developed; when this method of progression has
reached its most advanced stage the fore-limb is freed
very thoroughly from its duties of support. Hopping is
a specialized development of the pronograde gait; and
it has led to some very interesting developments which

have a bearing upon the present study. To these hopping animals we will return.

We will now come back to our primitive Mammal with its four mobile limbs, and picture it taking, not to a terrestrial, but to an arboreal life. I imagine that the first stages of this advance could be pictured as being built upon the ability the animal already possessed of surmounting such obstacles as chanced to lie in its terrestrial path. The ability which such a primitive Mammal would have for climbing might perhaps be gauged by having regard for that skill in clambering which is manifested in the tailed Amphibians, a skill which we must remember develops within the limits of their own Phylum (in the Tree Frogs) into perhaps the most perfected tree-climbing displayed in the Vertebrate series. It may seem a long way to go back when attempting to unravel the influences of tree-climbing among the Primates, to appeal to the clambering activities of the water-newt. And yet the anatomical condition of the limbs of Man demands a shifting backward of the inquiry to some such stage as this. I believe that the truest picture of the evolution of Primate climbing starts with such a scene as we are depicting now. The method of this amphibian or reptilian clambering must be appreciated, for, as we shall see, climbing may be conducted in several different ways; and the particular method practised by any animal may serve to date the evolutionary stage at which the habit was adopted. An Amphibian, or unspecialized Reptile, ascends an obstacle by clambering up; its feet are applied to the surface of the obstacle up which it clambers. It makes no attempt to obtain a grip by nails or claws, but it trusts merely to the apposition of its feet to the surface to which it clings, and when this fails the animal falls.

Two points must be especially noticed. As its progress continues, it repeatedly reaches ahead with one or other of its fore-limbs for a new hold, and whilst doing this its body weight is temporarily thrown upon its hind-limbs. And, again, in reaching out its fore-limb, the freedom of rotation possessed by the second segment of the limb allows the animal to apply the palmar surface of its " hand " against any new hold which may present itself at almost any angle.

From such a humble beginning great developments are possible; and here we may observe that, without the apprenticeship served in this lowly clambering, short cuts to tree-climbing have never attained the same ultimate perfection. As arboreal life becomes more complete, the search for a new foothold will become a far more exacting business than it is in the mere clambering we have pictured. The more exacting this search becomes, the more will there tend to be developed that most important factor—*the specialization of the functions of the fore and hind limbs*. While the animal reaches about with its fore-limb, the hind-limb becomes the supporting organ. With the evolution of this process there comes about a final liberation of the fore-limb from any such servile function as supporting the weight of the body : it becomes a free organ full of possibilities, and already capable of many things. This process I am terming *the emancipation of the fore-limb*, and its importance as an evolutionary factor appears to me to be enormous.

It will be noted that in the little picture we have drawn of the process, we have, as it were, rescued the fore-limb; rescued it while still possessed of all its inherited power of mobility, saved it from becoming an organ of mere stability, and handed it over to an enterprising mammalian stock to adapt to its needs.

This picture may seem fanciful, and yet in reality it is not so. I have thought it worth while to draw it thus, since, without such a picture, there are many things very difficult to understand. I will instance two such cases. We have hurried almost breathlessly over the process we have pictured, in a mental anxiety to arrive at emanci-

2

pation of the fore-limb before the limb had lost any of its possibilities of mobility. This we have done because of the knowledge that once the limb has become a supporting organ, and given up its birthright of mobility for the acquired stability, no subsequent degree of liberation, due to altered habits, will achieve the same great possibilities in evolution. Animals have liberated fore-limbs already made stable, or partially stable, and they have not attained the great results which we shall follow in the stock we have been picturing. It is thus with the jumping animals we have mentioned previously. The liberation of the fore-limb may be very complete, but it is a fore-limb of restricted possibilities that has been liberated.

The arboreal habit alone is not the talisman; other mammalian stocks have taken to an arboreal habit; but they have taken to it after varied periods of quadrupedal life. They have taken to it too late to derive the full benefits from it, for they took to it with the fore-limbs already deprived of some of their inherited mobility. Such animals never become perfect tree-climbers. They may acquire an extraordinary skill in running about the branches of trees as many Rodents do, or they may even climb in the proper sense of the word, but in this climbing the grip is not obtained by the application of the palmar surface of the hand, but by the hook-like action of claws and nails; this method is practised by many of the Carnivora. The maximum of possibilities is not attainable in any of these cases. It is not enough to have a thoroughly emancipated fore-limb, it is not enough to be thoroughly arboreal. It was a combination of seemingly humble and unimportant circumstances, acting at the very dawn of mammalian life, which permitted the emancipation of an unmodified fore-limb in a certain stock, and so laid the direct path for the evolution of the highest Mammals, and Man.

CHAPTER III

THE DEVELOPMENT OF THE POWER OF GRASP

WE have noted that the primitive animal we have been picturing could place the palm of its hand against any new hold with which it came into contact, and that the power of rotation possessed by its forearm enabled this contact to take place at a variety of angles. Its palms, for instance, may both be turned inwards so that a branch or other object can be held between their two opposed surfaces. This is a power which remains in the possession of many animals even after they have lost much of the primitive mobility of the fore-limb in quadrupedal life. As a general rule, the hopping animals and the semi-arboreal animals retain sufficient mobility to do this. Some of them can hold their food pressed between the two palms, and so are enabled to sit up and eat food held between their fore-paws. Others, which cannot attain to this, yet preserve sufficient mobility of the fore-limb to enable them to use it for a variety of minor purposes. The more thoroughly quadrupedal the animal is, the less is it able to turn its fore-limb to these minor uses. Familiarly, we may note that the typically quadrupedal dog will use its hind-feet for scratching, even the fore-end of its body; while the cat will scratch and wash its face with its fore-foot. But we are dealing, in possibilities, with something far bigger and more important than such things as these. We must not forget that in rescuing the fore-limb in its primitive mobile stage, before quadru-pedal life had in any way impaired its power of rotation, we saved not only a primitive second segment, but a

19

primitive third segment as well. We may now say that
we have rescued the third segment as a hand, and so
preserved it from ever becoming a mere paw or a hoof.
This is most important—perhaps as important a thing
as ever happened in any evolutionary story—for the
permanent preservation of a primitive hand, affixed to
a primitive rotating forearm, made possible a great
number of the most far-reaching developments.

By a primitive hand we mean a very definite thing,
and one essential in the make-up of this hand is the
possession of five separate, and fairly equally developed,
digits.   We have made use of the water-newt to picture
some stages of fore-limb development, but we may not
press comparisons with this type into minute details.
The hand of existing Amphibians does not fulfil all the
demands of our definition, for only four digits are present
in living tailed members, and four well-developed digits,
with a rudiment of a fifth, in living tailless forms.   But
there are several extinct forms of generalized Amphibia
and Reptilia which had what we may truly term a primitive hand, and among the living and unspecialized
Reptilia it is still to be met with.   It is a very remarkable fact that in the numerical development of the
individual bones which compose the separate fingers, the
Chelonians (Tortoises and Turtles) are the match of
Man and his nearest mammalian neighbours.   There is
evidently something extraordinarily primitive about the
hand that has been preserved and passed on to Man; but
like the primitive rotating forearm, this primitive, simple
and unspecialized five-fingered hand is full of possibilities.
These possibilities are given their chance of development,
and are made the most of under the circumstances we
are picturing—circumstances which include the emancipation of the fore-limb as one of the effects of the dawn
of arboreal life.   This primitive hand possesses muscles
which can move it upon the ulna and radius at the wrist-
joint, and muscles which can bend the fingers in towards

the palm (flexors), and others which can straighten them
out again (extensors). It is these finger muscles which
now become so important. We have noticed that some
of the less perfect tree-climbers run with great skill about
the branches, and that others climb rather than run,
but they obtain a grip by the specialized use of nails or
claws. It is a characteristic of the pioneer tree-climbers
we are picturing that they begin to grasp by the flexion
of their fingers, and obtain their grip, not by claws or
foot-pads or nails, but by an actual approximation of
the hand and the fingers to the objects up which they
desire to climb.

The power to grasp with the hand and fingers seems
such a very simple accomplishment that it is difficult to
realize how such an apparently trivial beginning can have
produced the tremendous changes that follow in its
train. In essence its beginning depends upon the preservation of a primitive second segment of the fore-limb,
for this has permitted the animal in its endeavours at
climbing to place the palmar surface of its hand and
fingers flat against the next hold for which it reaches out.
The mobility of the second segment already allows of
an adjustment of the hand to the object encountered.
Next, the hand by virtue of its flexor muscles makes the
adjustment more complete. In this way we may imagine
the fingers are closed over smaller branches, and the
animal begins to grasp. Although the picture is entirely
fanciful, we may imagine that the higher the animal
climbs (the more perfectly arboreal it becomes), the
smaller the branches encountered, and so the more perfect the adjustment of the finger grasp. This picture,
although it may be dismissed as thoroughly outside the
precise demands of science, is nevertheless a useful one,
since in dealing with the modifications of such a primitive
fore-limb it is perfectly true to say that the more thoroughly an animal becomes an arboreal creature, the more
perfect becomes its hand grasp. The animal now reaches

out with its fore-limb, throws its body weight temporarily upon its hind-limbs, and then with its hand catches hold of something ahead, and so helps to raise its body. This is true tree-climbing. It is a critical stage in evolution. The power of the hand grasp has made possible the fore-runners of the Primates, has perfected the evolution of the Primates, and paved the way for the development of Man.

At first, one would suppose this newly acquired power to be used solely for grasping the branches in arboreal progression, for catching hold of objects ahead, and for hanging on whilst a new foothold is secured. But with its developing perfection we may imagine the grasp used for other purposes, and some of these purposes we will enumerate here, but will discuss in detail later.

The animal, from grasping branches, may readily turn to grasping leaves and fruit—it may learn to grasp its food in its hand. As a sequel it may learn to convey the food so grasped to its mouth with its hand, and so become a hand-feeder.

It may take to grasping other objects which come in its way. These objects may be useful for food or they may not; but the animal will learn to form an estimate of the object grasped. As a sequel it may learn to feel, and to test novel objects with its hand. Again, the mother may learn to grasp her offspring in the precarious circumstances of an arboreal infancy; and she may adopt the habit of carrying and nursing her baby. All these things are of vast importance, and will be discussed according to the headings under which they appropriately fall.

CHAPTER IV

THE SKELETON OF THE FORE-LIMB

WHAT exactly we are to regard as the most simple condition of the actual skeletal structures of the fore-limb of the primitive land-living Vertebrate is, of course, open to some doubt; that we shall not be very far wrong in assuming it to be generally similar to that which is present in the most generalized Amphibians and Reptiles is certain. At the time of mammalian divergence from the Therapsid ancestor, we may assume the limb to be of this primitive Reptilian type, with the added tendency to a general lengthening, to which Broom has attached so much importance. In such a primitive limb there is a proximal *humerus* free to move upon the pectoral girdle at the shoulder-joint. The next segment consists of a pre-axial *radius* and a post-axial *ulna*, both bones articulating with the humerus at the elbow-joint, and at that joint both are flexed and extended on the humerus. Each bone is free of the other, so that movements of rotation can take place between them. Both bones of the second segment articulate with the first row of the carpal bones, so that although the hand is flexed and extended on the forearm, it is rotated with the forearm.

Discussions as to what is the primitive condition of the carpus, and how this primitive condition has been departed from in different types, open up the possibilities for widely divergent views. We will here adopt the oldest and simplest teaching—that of Gegenbaur, which is backed by the greatest weight of evidence.

Three bones enter into the formation of the first row

23

of the carpus—a pre-axial bone (*radiale*), an intermediate bone (*intermedium*), and a post-axial bone (*ulnare*). The second row is composed of five small and fairly uniform bones (Carpalia I.-V.), one being situated at the base of each metacarpal. Between the two rows, and situated in the middle of the carpus, is a central element (*centrale*). (We may, in modern morphology, be forced to depart slightly from the classical scheme of Gegenbaur, in admitting the possible presence of more than one *centrale*, but this possibility does not detract from the simplicity of the main plan.)

As to the number of rays in the distal segment of the limb, we know that among the lowest Vertebrates which lead aquatic lives they may be extremely numerous; in the most primitive of the higher land-living classes this is changed, and the possession of five terminal elements has become the rule. This change is undoubtedly associated with the development of extra-neural ribs and the formation of intra-costal limb plexuses, the number of epiblastic segments entering into the limb plexuses being now restricted to five, represented by the five roots entering into the formation of the brachial plexus. These five terminal digits are composed of a series of separate jointed elements, *metacarpals* and *phalanges*, of which there are primitively (or at any rate in very primitive types, if not in basic form) one metacarpal and three phalanges, or four separate elements, in each digit (see Fig. 6).

Taking the Mammalia as a whole, and selecting from any and every type the most unaltered feature of every segment of the limb, regardless of the condition of the other segments, we may estimate the amount of minimal departure from this archætype consistent with that stage of evolution represented by the Mammalia. The skeletal elements of the first and second segments may persist quite unaltered in a large number of Mammals.

The bones of the first row of the carpus and the os

centrale may remain in the ideal condition. The bones of the second row invariably show a fusion between carpale IV. and carpale V. into the *unciform* bone. The primitive five digits may persist, but an invariable reduction takes place in the elements composing the pollex, which consists of only three segments instead of the ideal four.

The immediate interest lies in the fact that these conditions of minimal departure from the primitive type are combined in the individual only within the limits of the Primates and those other animals which we believe to be immediately related to them (see Fig. 7). All other Mammals, though retaining primitive features of

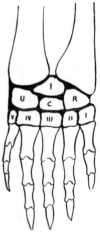

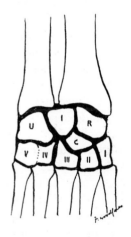

FIG. 6.—THE SKELETON OF THE HAND OF A WATER TORTOISE (*Chelydea serpentina*). (AFTER GEGENBAUR.)

FIG. 7.—THE CARPUS AS IT EXISTS IN SOME PRIMATES.

The os centrale is a separate element.

the fore-limb here and there, show in some other respects wider departures from the ideal.

Among the Primates we have skeletal fore-limb elements so little altered from the ideal type that the humerus and ulna and radius remain in their primitive condition. The first row of the carpal bones articulates with both ulna and radius, and consists of all the ideal elements; radiale (*scaphoid*), intermedium (*semilunar*), and ulnare (*cuneiform*) are all separate and normal. The os centrale is present. Carpale I. (*trapezium*), carpale II. (*trapezoid*), and carpale III. (*os magnum*) are separate, and not greatly changed; carpale IV. and carpale V. are fused into the *unciform*. The five digits are all present in a very primitive condition, the pollex alone lacking one of its elements. In addition to these slight modifications an ulnar sesamoid (*pisiform*) is present.

Now all these departures from the ideal which are manifested in the Primate fore-limb are modifications which have their parallels in very generalized Reptilia. Fusion of carpale IV. and V. takes place even in the very generalized chelonian carpus; in the same forms also is seen the identical loss of an element in the pollex, and the development of an ulnar sesamoid. Two additional modifications are present in Man and the giant Anthropoids (see Fig. 8). The centrale is lost as a separate element by fusion with the scaphoid (*radiale*) in Man, the Gorilla and the Chimpanzee; this, again, is a feature of some of the Lemurs and of so primitive a carpus as that seen in the Chelonia.

Persistence of the os centrale in the human carpus is not an exceptionally rare anomaly, and many cases have been recorded by Gruber. Rosenberg has also shown its normal presence in the human embryo. Anomalies of the Gorilla and Chimpanzee are naturally less well known than are those of Man, but even in these animals the os centrale is known to occur exceptionally. In the orang-utan and in the Gibbon it is normal and well developed.

In Man, Gorilla, Chimpanzee and Orang-utan the ulna does not directly articulate with the carpus, but is excluded from contact with the cuneiform (*ulnare*) by the

intervention of the triangular fibro-cartilage. This condition is not found in any of the more primitive forms and
must be regarded as a new and possibly progressive
feature.

It is a fact which cannot be ignored, that in the details
of its skeletal elements the fore-limb of the highest of

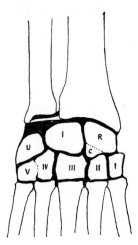

Fig. 8.—The Elements of the Carpus as present in Man,
in the Gorilla, Chimpanzee and Some Lemurs.

The os centrale is not normally present as a separate element.

the Mammals finds its likeness among living Vertebrates
in such a primitive creature as the Tortoise. Without
indulging to the full the speculations which such a fact
may prompt, we are justified in saying that the Primates
have retained a fore-limb skeleton that is singularly like
that with which we have every reason to believe the
ancestral Mammal was endowed.

CHAPTER V

THE CLAVICLE

ONE other skeletal element of the fore-limb needs brief mention, and this is the collar-bone, or clavicle, which is so well developed in Man. Although the homologues of the clavicle are perhaps more debated than those of any other bone in the body, it is not proposed to enter into any discussion regarding the respective merits of those theories which find the caudal homologue of the clavicle now in one, and now in another, element of the pelvic girdle. Here the clavicle will be regarded, as the work of Fawcett appears clearly to indicate, as an element peculiar to the fore-limb girdle. We will assume that the bone of the clavicle is an intramuscular ossification, making its appearance in the embryo first (at any rate in the Mammals), by two ossific centres, the one (lateral) in the deltoid-trapezius muscle sheet, and the other (median) in the pectoralis-sterno-cleido-mastoid sheet. These two ossific intramuscular intersections become continuous, and, in its complete development, the bony bar thus formed articulates at its median end with the sternum and at its lateral end with the shoulder girdle proper. We will further assume that this bony bar is a purely functional development, that it is laid down as a firm strut which keeps the shoulder girdle poised at the sides of the body, and which makes an acting point for the separated muscles that are derived from the sheets in which it is laid down (see Fig. 9). As such a strut, the clavicle is a very ancient possession of the Vertebrates. It occurs in the Dipnoi and certain other primitive fish

28

It may in some fishes become complicated by other struts not primitively parts of the shoulder girdle, or it may strut the shoulder girdle, not to the sternum, but to the skull, or to some outlier of it. A clavicular strut derived from dermal bone is present also in the majority

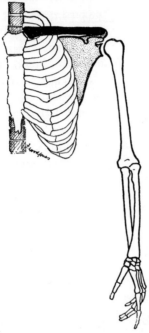

FIG. 9.—THE HUMAN SHOULDER GIRDLE, TO SHOW THE STRUT ACTION OF THE CLAVICLE.

of the Amphibians and Reptiles. Within the limits of these groups great range of variation in development is seen; the dermal struts may attain great complexity, or they may be altogether absent, and, on the whole, a functional rather than a systematic cause underlies the degree and condition of their presence. The dermal strut occurs again in the lowest Mammals, and here in perfect reptilian complexity of structure, the condition present in the Prototheria (Duck-billed Platypus, etc.)

being likened by all comparative anatomists to that in the typical pre-mammalian Vertebrates. In the rest of the mammalian orders the appearance of the clavicle,

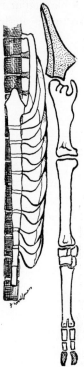

if we take the systematic position of the animal as our guide, can only be described as haphazard. Among the Metatheria (Marsupials), only *Perameles* (the Bandicoot) fails to possess a clavicle. Among Eutheria (higher Mammals), a complete clavicle is present in all Insectivora, except the aberrent aquatic *Potamogale;* it is present in some Edentata, in all Cheiroptera, and all Primates. It is entirely absent in Cetacea and Sirenia and Ungulata (see Fig. 10); in most Carnivora it appears only as a rudiment, though in some members of this order it attains a fair degree of development; in the Rodentia it is sometimes well developed and sometimes entirely absent. The only underlying principle which seems to explain the rather random development of this bone in different Mammals appears to be found in the functional demands made upon the movements of the fore-limb. So long as no more demand is made than the

FIG. 10.—THE SHOULDER GIRDLE OF AN UNGULATE, TO SHOW THE ABSENCE OF THE CLAVICLE.

The fore-limb has no strut to keep it poised at the side of the thorax.

simple backward and forward movement at the shoulder-joint, such as is seen in the walking and trotting of pure quadrupeds, this strut is either not developed, or attains no greater perfection than that of a mere isolated intermuscular ossification. Even the simple use of the fore-limb as a paddle is carried out in the absence of any strut, and the clavicle fails to be developed in aquatic paddlers. It is the wider range of movements of the shoulder-joint, such as culminates in the free action of circumduction, that preserves in full functional development this primitive vertebrate heritage in the mammalian shoulder girdle.

Within the groups Carnivora and Rodentia, it is easy to see that freedom of fore-limb and clavicular development go hand in hand. It is safe to assert that a Mammal possessing a fore-limb which, from any cause whatever, has become in any considerable degree emancipated from the function of mere quadrupedal progression will also possess a clavicle of fairly complete development, no matter what the systematic zoological position of the Mammal may be.

Emancipation of the fore-limb has preserved the clavicle, inherited in the general vertebrate make-up of the first mammalian type, and has insured its survival in a simple yet very perfect form in Man.

The arboreal habit, as the great factor in preserving and increasing the original mobility of the fore-limb, has also been the great factor in preserving in the human shoulder girdle a well-developed collar-bone.

CHAPTER VI

THE MUSCLES OF THE FORE-LIMB

TURNING from the skeletal features of the fore-limb to the arrangement of its muscles, we again meet a like condition of extremely primitive characters in the typical Primate and in Man. Although most authorities are agreed as to the general primitive condition of the human arm and hand—and it is difficult for an osteologist to find anything other than a very primitive arrangement in the general plan of the bones—yet the myologist has as a rule looked upon human musculature from rather a different standpoint. This is not the place to make detailed criticisms of the methods employed in comparative myology; but one might say that if the human fore-limb muscles are compared with those of a typical quadrupedal Mammal, then certain great changes will be found. It is easy to assume that since Man is a " high " form, and the horse, for instance, is a " low " one, then the fore-limb muscles of Man have advanced considerably in evolution. This type of reasoning permeates the study of comparative myology, and its fallacy needs no exposing since it is self-evident. If there is any truth in the present thesis, that the human stock has never been quadrupedal, never possessed four equally supporting limbs, then it is likely that the arrangement of muscles found in the human limb will have its near counterpart in some very primitive Vertebrate. It is likely that the muscles and the bones will follow exactly the same story. I think it is perfectly obvious that they do. Far from seeing any signs that the derivation of the muscular plan of the human arm is from that seen in any lower quadrupedal form, it seems quite obvious that the truly quadrupedal pronograde type is derived from a primitive arrangement such as is retained in Man.

We have an excellent account of a very generalized vertebrate type of musculature in the description given by Humphry of *Cryptobranchus japonicus*, and to the stage of evolution of the limb musculature as seen in this Amphibian we shall have to make frequent reference. The group of muscles which especially interests us here is that which produces the rotatory movements of the second segment of the limb, and in order to limit the purely anatomical details we will follow the history of those rotators which produce the movement of pronation —*i.e.*, turn the back of the hand upwards. This group is of primary importance, since it produces that mobility of the second segment which, as we have seen, is incompatible with true quadrupedal stability. The pronators compose a primitive group of muscles which shows the effects of alteration of function in a very definite manner; the condition of the members of the group is easily determined in different animal types, and their disposition may therefore be taken as a handy index of the degree to which mobility has been sacrificed to stability in the forearm. In *Cryptobranchus* this muscle group is well developed; but, as is the case with all the muscle groups of this very generalized animal, it is not so definitely subdivided into its component elements as it is in higher forms (see Fig. 11).

The pronators of this Amphibian consist of a superficial part, which arises from the ulnar condyle of the humerus in common with the M. flexor carpi radialis, but, dissociating itself from the common mass, is inserted into the lateral margin of the radius. Beneath this portion is a deeper set of fibres, which at its insertion to the radius becomes continuous with another sheet which

3

arises from the ulna. This sheet, which passes from the
ulna to the radius, is oblique in direction above, but
more transverse nearer to the wrist, where it becomes
continuous with another set of fibres, which, arising from
the ulna, passes to the radial side of the wrist and hand.

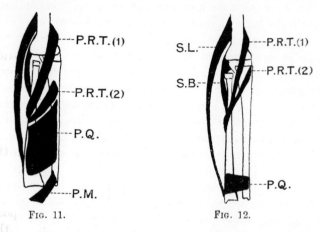

FIG. 11.   FIG. 12.

FIG. 11.—DIAGRAMMATIC FIGURE OF THE PRONATOR GROUP OF
MUSCLES IN *Cryptobranchus.*

P.R.T. (1), Mammalian superficial head of pronator radii teres.
P.R.T. (2), Deep Mammalian head of same muscle. P.Q.,
Pronator quadratus. P.M., Pronator manus.

FIG. 12.—DIAGRAM OF THE PRONATOR MUSCLES IN MAN.

P.R.T. (1), Superficial, humeral, head of pronator radii teres.
P.R.T. (2), Deep, ulnar, head of same muscle. P.Q., Pronator quadratus. S.L., Supinator longus. S.B., Supinator
brevis.

There is therefore in this generalized animal a more
or less continuous pronator sheet, the proximal part of
which is superficial, and passes from humerus to radius,
where it blends with an intermediate part. This second
part is deeper, and passes from ulna to radius, and, in its
turn, blends with a distal part which passes from the
ulna to the radial side of the third segment of the limb.
From this unspecialized condition, advance takes place,

as is the general rule, by the segmentation of muscular
sheets into separate muscles; and a comparison may be
made directly between this simple type and the more
specialized condition seen in some other animals. The
superficial portion of the proximal mass becomes the
humeral head of the M. pronator radii teres. The deep
portion of this mass, which is blended with the intermediate sheet, becomes the M. pronator intermedius,
or ulnar head of the M. pronator radii teres. The distal
mass, or M. pronator manus, looses its insertion to the
third segment in many forms, and, united with the lower
portion of the intermediate sheet, it constitutes the
M. pronator quadratus.

With the differentiation of the muscular sheets of
Cryptobranchus there is therefore afforded a myological
basis for (1) a bicipital M. pronator radii teres, and (2) a
definite M. pronator quadratus, which may, or may not,
possess extensions downwards to the carpus.

This is the condition found in many unspecialized
Reptiles and Amphibians, as well as in the most primitive
Mammals, and it may be regarded as the simplest type
of resolution of the primitive muscle sheets.

But if this condition of the pronator group may be
regarded as primitive, it is obviously one that is very
readily departed from at the dictates of functional
demands for the stability of the limb, and one that has
a very limited representation among the existing
mammalian types.

To gain an insight into the possible modifications of
this muscle group it will be best to take each muscle
separately; and the most simple comparison may be
made in the apparently illogical order of taking the
human condition first.

The M. pronator radii teres is a typical bicipital muscle
in Man. The superficial, and larger, portion arises from
the medial aspect of the lower end of the humerus; the
deeper, and smaller, portion is derived by a tendon from

the coronoid process of the ulna (see Figs. 13 and 14).
Between these two heads of origin the median nerve

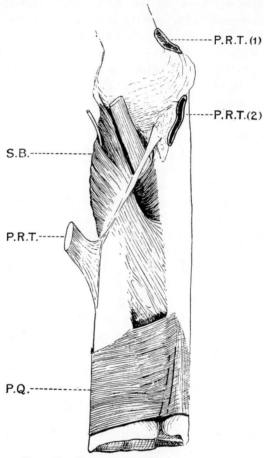

FIG. 13.—PRONATOR MUSCLES OF MAN.

P.R.T. (1), Site of origin of superficial head, and P.R.T. (2), of
the deep head of the pronator radii teres, the insertion of
which is at P.R.T. P.Q., Pronator quadratus. S.B., Supinator brevis.

passes into the forearm, thereby rendering the two
portions quite distinct. The deeper (ulnar) part is

variable in the degree of its development in Man; at times it constitutes but a small portion of the whole muscle, and occasionally it is entirely absent. In all

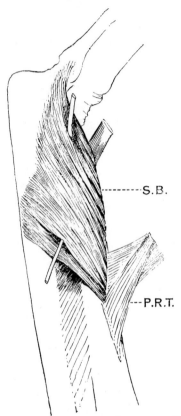

FIG. 14.—THE INSERTION OF THE BICIPITAL PRONATOR RADII
TERES OF MAN (P.R.T.).

S.B., Supinator brevis.

the Anthropoids this variability of the ulnar part is displayed, with an increasing tendency to vary in the direction of partial or complete absence.

In the Orang-utan the condition is practically identical with that seen in Man. In the Chimpanzee, Hepburn described the ulnar head as normally present; but Keith has shown that it is absent in as many as 10 per cent. of all examples dissected. Absence of the ulnar head is more usual in the Gorilla; Hepburn regarded complete absence as normal, but Keith has determined that it was present, in some degree, in about 40 per cent. of all individuals.

In none of the Monkeys is an ulnar head present under normal conditions, and the Lemurs are alike in this respect (see Fig. 15).

The ulnar head is absent in all other orders of Eutherian Mammals, with the exception of at any rate some of

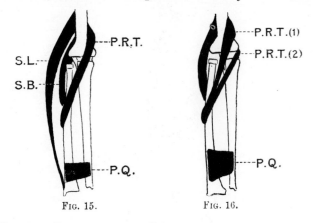

FIG. 15.

FIG. 16.

FIG. 15.—DIAGRAM OF THE PRONATOR MUSCLES IN TYPICAL PRIMATES.
Lettering as before.

FIG. 16.—DIAGRAM OF THE PRONATOR MUSCLES IN A TREE SHREW (*Tupaia ferruginea*).
Lettering as in other diagrams.

the Insectivora. In the Tree Shrews (*e.g.*, *Tupaia ferruginea*) there is (despite Kloster's assertion to the contrary) a portion of the muscle deep to the median nerve, and this portion arises from the upper extremity of the ulna and from the internal collateral ligament of the elbow-joint (Figs. 16 and 17). In an Oriental Pygmy Shrew (*Crocidura bottigi*), again, the muscle is in

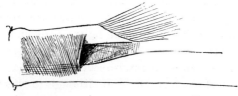

FIG. 17.—THE PRONATOR QUADRATUS AND INSERTION OF PRONATOR RADII TERES IN *Tupaia ferruginea.*

its bicipital form (Fig. 18). In all the Metatherian Mammals the only origin of the M. pronator radii teres is from the humerus, the ulnar head being absent. In

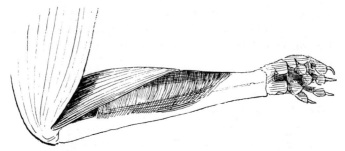

FIG. 18.—THE PRONATOR RADII TERES AND PRONATOR QUADRATUS IN A CROCIDURINE SHREW.

the lowly Monotremes the human deep head has been asserted to be present, but it cannot be regarded as a normal component of the muscle.* Among the Reptilia

* At the time of delivering the lecture I relied upon the latest paper published upon the subject—that by Gordon Taylor and Victor Bonney (*Jour. Anat. and Phys.*, vol. 40, p. 34)—which definitely asserted the presence of the ulnar head in Ornithorhynchus and in Echidna. Since that time I have dissected the fore-limbs of two examples of Ornithorhynchus and one Echidna (kindly placed at my disposal by Dr. W. C. McKenzie), and I find no trace of an ulnar head in any of these specimens, the condition agreeing with that described by Rud. Kloster ("Anatomische Hefte," 1901, p. 671).

the same condition is found; an ulnar head constitutes a bulky portion of the muscle in the Chelonia (*e.g.*, *Testudo*) and in the Lacertilia (*e.g.*, *Varanus*). Among the generalized Amphibia, *Cryptobranchus* shows the same thing in the ill-differentiated form we have noted previously.

The story of the M. pronator quadratus is equally striking. In Man an interosseous membrane unites the two bones of the forearm, and although in this membrane there is, as is usual in such membranes, a crossed arrangement of its fibres, nevertheless the great bulk of the strands run from the radius down to the ulna. On a plane altogether anterior to this membrane the muscle bundles of the M. pronator quadratus run on the whole in an opposed direction, from ulna down to radius. It is important to notice that behind the M. pronator quadratus the interosseous membrane is quite uninterrupted; the muscle does not replace the membrane, but lies in front of it.

This condition is typical of all the Primates. It is found in some of the more mobile-limbed members of other Eutherian orders. It is present in *Tupaia* and in *Crocidura*, in typically human guise; and it is present again in generalized Reptiles and in Amphibia. Its condition in *Cryptobranchus* has previously been mentioned.

A true M. pronator quadratus is not present in those thoroughly quadrupedal animals in which the rotation of the two bones of the second segment is lost. The true M. pronator quadratus is not to be confused with the M. radio-ulnaris, which is a purely interosseous muscle, homologue of the M. tibio-fibularis of the leg, and is situated on a plane posterior to the fibres of the distinct M. pronator quadratus.

The facts of the occurrence of these muscles in the Vertebrate series must be admitted to be very curious, since the typically human condition is such a rare mammalian feature, and yet is one so closely matched among the generalized Amphibia and Reptilia. The facts may

be interpreted in two ways—the human condition may
be a new and gradual development from the stage seen
in the typical lower Eutherian Mammals, or it may be
a retention of an extremely primitive and generalized
vertebrate type of musculature. Most authorities upon
comparative anatomy appear to regard the ulnar head
of the M. pronator radii teres as a new development in
the Anthropoids—a development which becomes most
fully established and most fully perfected in Man. This
development is, by many, regarded as a reversion. This
point of view was taken by Gordon Taylor and Victor
Bonney, and they have concluded regarding this muscle:
" It may be objected that it appears rather strange that
in Man, a Mammal most highly specialized, and the most
highly evolved, the apparently older stage in evolution
of the muscle persists. But we must remember that in
him movement between the bones of the forearm has
reappeared in an extreme degree." Were the human
condition of this muscle to be an isolated phenomenon,
perhaps such an attitude might be justified; but when
the primitive type of every bone and joint of the human
fore-limb is taken into account, we must hesitate before
we name these things as " reappearances " in Man.
That the human ulnar head of the M. pronator radii teres
is a retention of a primitive type appears to me to be a
more reasonable view when all the facts of the anatomy
of the fore-limb are taken into consideration. I therefore
regard this muscle of Man as being more akin to the
ancestral type than anything seen in the rest of the
living members of the Primates.

As for the human M. pronator quadratus, it is usually
regarded as being only a partial survival of a primitively
extensive interosseous muscle, which is best developed
in quadrupedal forms. We have previously pointed out
that the interosseous muscle (M. radio-ulnaris) is on a
plane which is deep to that occupied by the true M.
pronator quadratus, and the nerve-supply points also to

their entire morphological separation. I do not think the facts justify us in regarding the human M. pronator quadratus as a degenerated portion of any muscle present in quadrupedal Mammals, but I imagine that this muscle, which produces rotation of the fore-limb bones, is absent in them, and is replaced by a muscle which braces the immobile bones firmly together. The human M. pronator quadratus finds its parallel in the same forms as does the deep head of the M. pronator radii teres, and I imagine that their story is the same, and that their retention is due to the same primitive nature of the forearm in these types.

It is probable that when all power of rotation of the forearm bones is lost, the ulnar head of the M. pronator radii teres, being useless under the circumstances, shifts its origin to the humerus, and joining into the superficial mass, acts with it as a flexor of the elbow-joint.

Regarded in this way, and solely from this point of view, the forearm of Man is more primitive than that of any living Primate except the Orang-utan; but it finds its match in the generalized Insectivora, in the Prototheria (in part), and in the unspecialized Reptiles and Amphibians, and this is a story very like that told by the bones themselves.

CHAPTER VII

THE FORE-LIMB: SUMMARY

IT would be a difficult matter to find the author who, writing of the human forearm and the human hand, has not seen in them the very highest and most perfect development of the fore-limb found anywhere in the animal kingdom. It has long been customary to lavish praise upon this culmination of human perfections, or climax of evolutionary advances, as writers of different periods have judged it. The divine plan was most surely to be seen in the human hand, that most wonderful of specially designed members. " The Construction of the Hand of Man " was especially chosen by the trustees of the Earl of Bridgwater as a subject in the expounding of which an apt writer could find outlet for almost inexhaustible eulogies, and for countless examples of perfection of design. It is, perhaps, to be doubted if Sir Charles Bell, in his completed Bridgwater Treatise, took full advantage of the wealth of material at his disposal, or of the insatiable popular appetite for authoritative statements upon the human perfections. Bell was so thorough an anatomist that it was impossible for him to restrain his admiration for the lion's paw and the horse's hoof—even the anatomical conditions of the despised sloth find in him an admirer; but although they are extremely elegant, his observations upon the *human* hand are not perhaps coloured with an enthusiasm so real as that which the noble patron himself entertained. " Were we to limit our inquiry to the bones of the arm and hand of Man, no doubt we should soon discover their

43

provisions for easy, varied, and powerful action, and conclude that nothing could be more perfectly suited to their purposes. But we must extend our views to comprehend a great deal more—a greater design." This, and many other similar passages, shows Bell's attitude in the work he did for his Bridgwater Treatise, and it is to be regretted that many lesser writers, who were untrammelled by the confines imposed by so narrowing a circumstance, did not follow Bell in this width of outlook. Those modern authors who have seen so much in the so-called "attainment of the erect position" (Munro) have been especially lavish in their praise of the human hand as a mere anatomical structure. Dr. Munro in his Presidential Address at the British Association in 1893 permitted himself the expression that the human hand is "the most complete and perfect mechanical organ Nature has yet produced." Such a statement on the part of an anatomist can only be attributed to enthusiasm, and to a failure to differentiate between the very primitive anatomical condition of the hand and the perfection of this simple mechanism when linked to a human brain. Even John Goodsir was more moderate, for he claimed no more than that "the human hand is the only perfect or complete hand."

The hand with its multitude of uses, its better suiting to human purposes than such a thing as a hoof or a paw, its apparent complexity and perfection of movement, was a thing so easily turned to as affording evidence of design—and by design was meant a special and divine planning. In 1833 almost any anatomist in the United Kingdom could have done the Bridgwater Treatise more to its purpose than did Sir Charles Bell. As things were, and with the height of apparent incongruity, the book he wrote in 1833 makes a very suitable introduction to the work of Darwin twenty-six years later.

After 1859 the forearm and hand, in common with every other feature of the human body, came to be

regarded, not as a wonderful and specially designed
structure, but as the perfected products of accumulated
ages of evolution—the last thing in animal development
and specialization. It is no overstatement of the case
to say that Man was regarded by many as the last thing
made, the culmination of evolution, and for some opponents of the new teaching and for some of its sup-
porters he was the most modern animal. The orthodox
chronology was accepted, the "highest" form was the
last form made, but instead of being the latest creation,
he was the latest evolution. Huxley soon exposed the
folly of this notion when it was definitely brought forward
by an opponent. But though the statement of the idea
as expressed by Mr. Gladstone may have been very crude,
and its demolition easy by such powers of argument as
were Huxley's, still, in more subtle guise the same idea
becomes presented under many forms even to-day, and
this not by any means necessarily from opponents of
evolution; in such forms its refutation is not always easy.
In even the most rigid and strictly scientific investigations
in comparative anatomy this tendency is at times manifested. The human type of joint, or nerve, or muscle, or
what not is so often assumed to be the last perfected—
the culminating type. There is a vague idea, which
insinuates itself in many ways, that the human type of
structure must be derived from, and have passed through,
stages seen in a series of "lower" animals. A foolish
argument may be permitted in dealing with a folly.
Were a horse capable of writing works on comparative
anatomy, he would probably, and with far more justice,
regard his race as being the last effort in evolutionary
chronology, and he would, and again with far more
justice, derive his highly specialized limbs from those of
some such primitive form as Man.

A Bridgwater Treatise upon "The Construction of the
Hoof of the Horse," followed by a "Descent of the
Horse" by a member of the same species, would be a

most healthy tonic for the human comparative anatomist
as well as for the human philosopher; in these two hypothetical works there is no doubt that the human fore-
limb would suffer badly. Far from being regarded as
the acme of evolutionary processes, it would be judged
as an extraordinary survival of a very primitive feature
far into the mammalian series, and more would be written
upon its striking similarity to the corresponding member
in the salamander and the tortoise than of its adaptation
to the multitude of human functions. This is a silly
argument, and no comparative anatomist not resident
in the kingdom of the Houyhnhnms would enter into
discussion with a quadruped that wrote a thesis showing
that the human fore-limb was very like that of a water-
newt. I have, however, brought the subject forward in
this way of set purpose, for as unbiassed judges of our-
selves we are to say definitely one way or the other:
Is the arrangement of bones and muscles we have seen
in the human arm a gradually elaborated evolutionary
perfection, or is it merely the retention of a condition so
primitive that it is matched only among its immediate
kin, and by types situated in the vertebrate stock right
at the point of mammalian divergence ? In anatomical
terms we may say: Have we lost a primitive arrangement
of bones and muscles, and then regained them, in evolution, upon exactly the same lines, or have we simply
retained them comparatively unaltered from the dawn
of mammalian specialization ? We must not overlook
in this the gravity of the second alternative, for it carries
with it the assumption that the human stock began to
be differentiated in that dawn period when the Mammals
themselves were evolved from some possible Theromorph
ancestor. With all the evidence that is available I cannot
see how it is possible to avoid this second conclusion.
In bones, and in muscles, the human fore-limb is far
more like that of a tortoise than it is like that of a horse
or a dog. This is no fanciful way of stating the case,

nor is it going one whit farther than the ordinarily gross facts of demonstrable anatomy warrant. Could we imagine an isolated human arm to be the only relic extant of the human race, and were this arm to be dissected by some superanatomist, he would find the arrangement of its skeletal and muscular elements matched very nearly in the Giant Apes and Old-World Monkeys, in some of the lowest Lemurs, and some primitive Insectivora, as well as in the more unspecialized Reptiles and some Amphibians; but he would search in vain for its like among the remaining mammalian groups.

CHAPTER VIII

THE FATE OF THE HIND-LIMBS

WE have hurriedly reviewed the process by which a primitive Mammal with four undifferentiated and mobile limbs achieved the emancipation of its fore-limb by its climbing activities. It is now necessary to make an attempt to follow the changes which take place in the hind-limb under the same circumstances. This phase is rather more complex in the hind-limb, and though the changes produced are not, perhaps, so great, their sequence has been more liable to interruption. The most primitive type of hind-limb we may imagine is an exact counterpart of the picture we have drawn of the fore-limb. It corresponds segment for segment, and joint for joint, with those described in the fore-limb. It has all the same possibilities; its fate depends in great measure upon the emancipation of the fore-limb. We have pictured the animal in its initial stages of tree-climbing as reaching out, with its fore-limb, to obtain new holds. It is during this oft-repeated interval that the fate of the hind-limb is determined, for, during this interval, it becomes *the* supporting limb upon which the body weight is thrown. Here is therefore the dawn of the differentiation in function of fore and hind limb; the fore-limb is reaching ahead for a new hold, the hind-limb is temporarily supporting the body during the act. It must be noted, however, that this supporting is of a very definite kind, and is not by any means of the same nature as that which is brought about in those animals which, being purely terrestrial, have become typically quadrupedal. In arboreal life, the hind-limb never becomes a mere stable prop; it becomes the principal support of the body weight, but it is a support which is bearing a body undergoing endless changes of poise.   Moreover, it is discharging this function among the branches of a tree; the foot is not resting on the ground, it is placed in apposition with a branch.   The sole of the foot becomes applied to the branch of a tree, in the same manner as does the palm of the hand.   The mobility of the second segment of the lower limb becomes limited and restricted to definite lines, but it does not become lost; the simple condition of the foot becomes retained even if not so completely as in the fore-limb.   The power of grasp of the foot is developed, though not to the degree of perfection which is seen in the hand.   We may imagine the evolutionary story to have been carried out somewhat on these lines. The animal pauses in its attempts to climb, it reaches for a new hold with its hands, and so trusts to its legs for its support.   Later, the power to grasp becomes more perfectly developed in the hand, and when it has secured a new hold it can grasp and suspend the body weight while the foot reaches farther ahead for a new foothold; a degree of mobility of the second segment of the leg is thus retained, and a degree of development of grasp with the foot is thus developed.   From the attainment of this stage, two divergent developments are possible.   The hind leg may develop a degree of mobility and of grasp equal, or almost equal, to that of the hand, a condition which fits the animal for the time-honoured distinction as quadrumanous or four-handed.   The foot may become, equally with the hand, a grasping and suspending organ; or the hand and forearm may be specialized as the mobile grasping-suspending organ, and the leg and foot as the supporting—still somewhat mobile and somewhat grasping—organ.   It is the grasping-supporting and not the grasping-suspending leg that has, from this common point of divergence, led to better things.

The one is characteristic of the higher, and the other of the lower, living members of the Primates. The most typically arboreal of the Lemurs know but little distinction of hand and foot; both are equally grasping-suspending organs, and as a consequence it matters little to the animal if it hangs or climbs head upwards or head downwards. *Nycticebus tardigradus* positively seems to prefer an inverted position, and I have noticed that, when perfect freedom of action is permitted, the animal nearly always suspends itself by its feet and hangs head downwards whilst it eats. When going to rest in the daytime, it will climb to the top of its cage, and then, turning round, go to sleep upside down like a bat. In resuming its activity towards evening, it releases the grasp of its hands, and carries out a careful examination of everything within its reach before it relaxes the grasp of its feet. *Nycticebus* will also grasp food and other objects with its foot, but shows nevertheless a decided preference for using its hand for this purpose. This specialization of the foot as a grasping organ has been carried still further in the New-World monkeys, and it has conferred upon that group the title Pedimana, or foot-handed, in the classification of some former zoologists. In the American monkeys, the development of the prehensile tail and specialization of the grasping foot at the expense of the grasping hand has played a very important part, and to this question we will return later. The higher Primates of the Old World, on the other hand, have differentiated the functions of the hind and fore limbs very thoroughly. They suspend themselves only by the fore-limbs, and use their hind-limbs solely for passive, but still grasping, support; they do not hang or climb head downwards. There is a homely, but not therefore necessarily unimportant, difference manifested in the arboreal activity of these two extremes in Primate life. A Lemur climbs up among the branches head first; *Nycticebus* ascends with extraordinary deliberation,

climbing hand over hand and testing every new hold
that it obtains before finally trusting its weight to it.
When it has reached the limit of its ascent, it commonly
turns round, and, hanging by its feet, eats its meal or
performs its toilet head downwards. It is from such a
position that it descends, and its descent is carried out
in exactly the same manner as its ascent, but naturally
in a reversed position—it crawls and climbs down head
forwards. All this is very easily watched in *Nycticebus*,
because its actions are so deliberately leisured and orderly,
but the same head forward descent is typical of all the
Lemurs I have had the opportunity of watching.

The New-World monkeys do the same thing, but in
them the use of the prehensile tails of some species rather
complicates the process of climbing down head foremost.
Now, it is an observation easily made wherever a higher
Old-World monkey is to be seen, that although it climbs
up a tree, it walks down again hind end foremost. Most
monkeys come down a tree just as a man does, bearing
the weight of the body by the suspending hand grasp
and by the supporting foothold. As a man descends
a ladder, so a higher monkey descends a tree. We may
sum up this process by saying that the lower Primates
climp up trees and climb down again, but the higher
Primates climb up and then walk down.

Now the difference shown in these two simple cases is
in reality a very great one. The arboreal habit conferred
its benefits by emancipating the fore-limb from the duties
of support and progression, and, by differentiating its
functions from that of the hind-limb, it saved the animal
from becoming quadrupedal. In differentiating the
functions of the two sets of limbs, the animal gains a
great deal. Some animals, one might almost say, have
gone too far in adapting themselves to the arboreal habit.
An animal, saved by the arboreal habit from becoming
quadrupedal, does not gain the maximum of the benefits
derivable from its new mode of life, if it is saved from

this fate only to become quadrumanous. Four feet do not lead far in the struggle for mammalian supremacy, four hands do not lead a great deal farther. It was the differentiation into two hands and two feet that provided the great strength of the stock from which Man arose.

The active specialization of the fore-limb did much, but it could not do all, without the accompanying passive specialization of the hind-limb. Mere ability in climbing which usurped the power of any real ability to walk, was but a poor accomplishment, for to complete the whole story of evolution the animal which climbed up the tree had still to walk down—and the Old-World apes still show in caricature how this was done.

CHAPTER IX

THE SKELETON OF THE HIND-LIMB

WE have seen that the human arm and hand exhibit a strikingly primitive anatomical picture, and that, on the whole, the resemblance of these parts of Man to the same parts of the rest of the Primates is very great. We have arrived at this conclusion despite the rather common assumption that in the hand of Man there is evinced the very highest human specialization and refinement. Compared with the fore-limb, the hind-limb is apt to be ranked as a rather primitive and unspecialized thing in Man. This assumption, again, is contrary to all the facts, for if we regard the hind-limb as presenting a more primitive condition in certain Primates (and this is a well-justified point of view), we must admit a very definite alteration from the primitive arrangement in the leg and foot of Man. The human hind-limb has specialized considerably from the condition seen in the arboreal Monkeys, and the arboreal hind-limb is, as we shall see, far nearer to the primitive Vertebrate type. Between the anatomical condition of the hind-limb of tho Anthropoids and that seen in Man there is apparently a somewhat sudden break in the story of the evolution of the leg. But the changes which ultimately become so characteristic of Man are already at work in the Gibbons, the Orang-utan, the Chimpanzee, and especially in the Gorilla. They are already apparent in some of the Old-World monkeys.

There will be no need to discuss at all fully the anatomical details of the primitive hind-limb, since the likeness to the fore-limb, which we have already touched on, is very great. There is a ventral meeting of the elements of the pelvic girdle at the pubic symphysis. This meeting of the ventral parts of the pelvic girdle subserves the functional rôle played by the clavicle in the anterior extremity, and this bone is not represented morphologically in the skeleton of the posterior extremity. The hip-joint obviously corresponds to the shoulder. The femur with its muscles recapitulates the features we have noted in the humerus, the knee-joint corresponds to the elbow.

The tibia and fibula, free to move on the femur at the knee-joint, and free to move upon each other, are the homologues of the radius and ulna (see Fig. 19). The ideal tarsus consists of nine bones: tibiale, intermedium and fibulare constituting the first row, tarsalia I.-V. the second, and an os centrale is included between the two rows, this condition obviously reproducing that we have already noted in the carpus. Five metacarpals and five digits with their appropriate muscles complete the architecture of the foot. The digits are composed (as in the hand) of three separate phalanges, and all the digits are well developed, with the middle one as the longest member of the series.

These are the features which we may presume to be present in the primitive hind-limb, and they will become modified, now in this direction and now in that, as function demands it.

There is a strong presumption that the hind-limb will depart more early than the fore-limb from this primitive condition, and this presumption is strongly borne out by the facts. From what we have seen of the effects of even minimal demands for a supporting function in the case of the fore-limb, we shall not expect to find a thoroughly primitive hind-limb at all far up in the land-living vertebrate stock. The hind-limb was called on, in the land-living Vertebrates, at the very dawn of mammalian specialization, as a support for the body weight. Stability became substituted at the outset of the story for

mobility. Environmental conditions could not combine
to free the hind-limb of its duty of supporting the body
weight and yet preserve it in full functional activity;
the arboreal habit did this for the fore-limb, but there
was no life circumstance that could do the same thing
for the hind-limb. An aerial life might, at first sight,

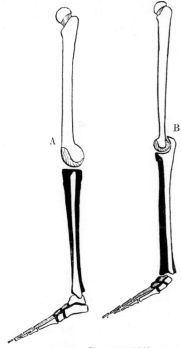

FIG. 19.—DIAGRAMMATIC COMPARISON OF THE SKELETAL
ELEMENTS OF (A) HIND AND (B) FORE LIMB.

seem to fulfil the necessary conditions, and flight might
seem to afford an escape from the supporting servitude
of the hind-limb. Flying Mammals have achieved many
interesting modifications in hind-limb structure, but they
have not successfully emancipated a hind-limb to give it
other and more highly educational functions. They have
avoided making it a mere prop only to convert it into a
suspending hook. The hind-limb of the Bats is worthy

of attention for its very special adaptations; but it is not a member destined to carry its owner far in the race for mammalian supremacy.

Only a purely aquatic life could produce an animal in which the hind-limb took no part whatever in the support of the body weight, and in the thoroughly aquatic forms (Sirenia and Cetacea) the hind-limb, deprived of this function, becomes a mere rudiment. Consequently, even in the most primitive of the prototherian Mammals, we find that the ideal condition is somewhat widely departed from. In the Monotremes the fibula is large, and from its proximal end a process rises above the point of articulation with the tibia, and both tibia and fibula are separated in their whole length; both bones of the second segment are preserved, and some degree of mobility between them still survives the demand for stability. The mobility of tibia and fibula upon each other is, however, best retained in the arboreal Metatheria, where, especially in *Phascolarctus* and some of the *Phalangers*, the power of rotation rivals that displayed between the radius and ulna. In the arboreal Sloths, again, the fibula is a large and well-formed bone which articulates with the tibia at its two extremities. In the Tree Shrews (*Tupaiadæ*) the fibula is well developed and entirely separated from the tibia, whereas in many terrestrial Insectivora it has become reduced and fused to its neighbour. In the Primate stock good development, complete separation, and even slight mobility of the fibula upon the tibia, are maintained as a part of the arboreal adaptation. In all other mammalian orders the fibula tends to undergo the reduction we have noted in the ulna of the fore-limbs of quadrupedal animals; all movement between it and the tibia is lost early, and the fibula becomes a rudiment finally blended into the structure of the dominant tibia.

No Mammal retains the ideal primitive tarsus, but the same may be said of existing Reptiles and even of their fossil representatives. The tibiale and intermedium are fused to form the astragalus, while the fibulare remains large and distinct as the calcaneum, thus reducing the first row to two bones. The centrale remains as the large scaphoid; tarsalia I., II., and III. persist as distinct elements, the inner, middle and external cuneiform bones; while tarsalia IV. and V. fuse into the cuboid. This constitutes the minimal mammalian reduction (and indeed the minimal reduction of existing Reptiles), and as such it is typical of the Primates (see Fig. 20). It is also seen in the Insectivora and in some other orders, but it is

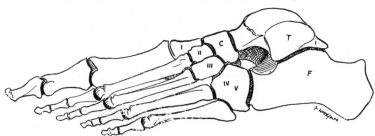

FIG. 20.—SKELETON OF THE HUMAN FOOT, TO SHOW THE FATE
OF THE PRIMITIVE ELEMENTS OF THE TARSUS.

carried farther by other fusions and reductions in most highly specialized quadrupedal Mammals.

The five primitive digits remain in their elemental development and relative proportions in the Primates, as well as in the Insectivora and some other orders, and, like the thumb, the big toe has undergone a reduction by the loss of one element. In most of the members of the Primate stock the primitive formula of the digits is retained, and the third or middle toe outstrips its neighbours as does the middle finger.

It may therefore be claimed for the typical Primate hind-limb that almost as far as original simplicity is retained in the Mammals it is here present in all the skeletal elements. In mobility of the second segment only is the Primate simplicity surpassed by the Monotremes and by the arboreal Metatheria.

CHAPTER X

THE MUSCLES OF THE HIND-LIMB

In the hind-limb we may make a brief review of those muscles which are the homologues of the rotators, the history of which we have followed in the fore-limb. The power of rotation of the second segment of the hind-limb is, as we have seen, very readily lost when any supporting function is demanded of the limb. This demand for support is made at the outset of terrestrial life, and, as a consequence, the rotator muscles of tibia and fibula undergo a change very early in the vertebrate series.

In *Cryptobranchus japonicus* there is a muscle which arises from the upper and outer aspect of the fibula, and is inserted to the inner border of the tibia at a lower level.

This muscle rotates the tibia around the fibula; it corresponds to the ulnar portion of the M. pronator radii teres of the arm, and it is named M. pronator tibiæ.

Superficial to this is a longer muscle, which, arising from the outer condyle of the femur, passes to the inner side of the foot. This muscle is the M. pronator pedis, and though the comparison cannot be maintained for all its connections, it contains the element homologous with the humeral portion of the M. pronator radii teres. In the hind-limb there is perhaps no true homologue of the whole of the M. pronator quadratus of human anatomy, but the M. accessorius is, in all probability, derived from an element equivalent to its lowest carpal fibres. The interosseous M. tibio-fibularis is present upon a deeper plane.

In *Varanus*, as an example of a reptilian form whose

limbs have taken on some part of the bodily support, the condition is as yet unchanged, so far as the fibular origin of the M. pronator tibiæ is concerned, and this muscle is found as (but perhaps only as part of) the M. popliteus of the higher Vertebrates. The superficial portion possesses practically no power of rotation, and the movement between the two bones is becoming somewhat more limited. Among the Mammals, the Monotremes and some of the less specialized Marsupials still possess the M. popliteus, which is the exact homologue of the deep, or ulnar, part of the M. pronator radii teres, for it arises from the upper end of the fibula, and is inserted into the tibia, upon which bone it produces some degree of rotation. Among some of the Insectivora, the M. popliteus is in a half-way stage, for it arises from the upper end of the fibula and from the capsule of the knee-joint. This is the case in some of the Shrews, and apparently also in *Chrysochloris*, the Golden Moles (Dobson). In the common Hedgehog (*Erinaceus*), the muscle has migrated still farther towards the femur, but it still arises from the capsule of the joint as well as from the femoral condyle. In some of the Lemurs, the M. popliteus still retains connection with the fibula through the intervention of a tendon and a sesamoid bone, just as it does in some Lizards; but in all other Primates the main origin is entirely from the femur, with occasional slight excursions to the ligaments of the joint. A small, deeper portion, the M. peroneo-tibialis, however, retains connection with the fibula, but this muscular slip is derived, in all probability, from the deeper interosseous muscle of the lower Vertebrates. In Man the popliteus muscle arises entirely from the femur, and even the peroneo-tibialis is only present in one out of some seven subjects, according to Gruber (see Fig. 21). The story of this muscle group appears to be fairly clear from the functional point of view. So long as the old mobility was retained, the rotator muscle passed from bone to bone across the second segment; but with the gradual loss of this mobility, and its substitution by stability, the muscle shifted its origin as its function changed, and, ascending via the capsule of the knee-joint, it joined the external condyle of the

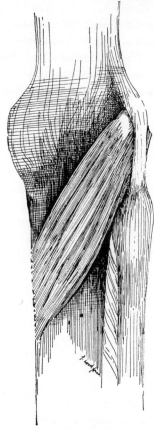

FIG. 21.—THE BACK OF THE HUMAN KNEE-JOINT, TO SHOW THE POPLITEUS MUSCLE.

femur. It then exchanged its rotating function for that of flexion of the knee-joint. This is a mere repetition of the story of the ulnar head of the M. pronator radii teres in those quadrupedal animals in which the fore-limb has suffered changes identical with those in the hind-limb.

The superficial portion of the M. pronator radii teres is represented in the leg by a muscle which has long since lost all power of rotation, and in Man is almost certainly merged with the lateral head of the calf muscle named M. gastrocnemius.

It is clear, therefore, that these muscle groups of the fore and hind limbs have undergone very dissimilar changes in Man. We have seen how strangely primitive is the retention of the condition of the arm; but it would seem that, in the leg, the primitive condition was departed from, and that some degree of support was demanded from the leg at an early stage in human evolution. With a simple arrangement of anatomical parts, a slight shifting of muscular origins has turned a perfectly mobile second segment into a supporting segment, constructed upon very simple lines. That these changes are those produced by the demands of support from the hind-limb in tree-climbing seems obvious, since they are present in all arboreal Primates, and as such we may imagine they have been long established in the ancestry of Man.

CHAPTER XI

OTHER ARBOREAL ADAPTATIONS OF THE HIND-LIMB

BESIDES the features which we have already noted in the arboreal hind-limb there are others of equal, or even greater, importance in the story of the evolution of Man as an arboreal animal. These other changes can only be referred to in outline, since the details of anatomical arrangements connected with them are legion. In picturing the early stages of the development of climbing, it was noted how the animal, supporting its body weight temporarily on its hind-limbs, reached out ahead for a new hold for its hands. This was the interval which marked the dawn of specialization of the functions of fore and hind limbs, and in which stability was demanded in some measure from the hind-limb. But in this interval another, and a very important, thing is happening, for as the animal reaches ahead, its body axis is altered, and the support of the hind-limbs is called upon in a very special manner. In this interval of climbing up, the body axis approaches the vertical, and the animal becomes in this way a temporary orthograde. There are degrees in this development of an orthograde habit, even if it be only a temporary phase, as in the primitive arboreal enterprise we are picturing. An animal may carry its body axis upright as a temporary expedient or as a life habit, while still retaining its thigh at right angles to its trunk; or it may hold its trunk erect upon an extended thigh.

There are many animals which can maintain the trunk

62

in a temporary position of uprightness upon a flexed thigh. A dog sitting up to beg, a squirrel eating its nut, or a bear awaiting its bun, are examples of this degree of uprightness. There are many animals which adopt this posture as a life habit, the Kangaroo (*Macropus*) and the Jerboa (*Dipus*) are good examples of Mammals which are habitually orthograde as far as their trunk axis is concerned, but in which the thigh is normally flexed so as to be nearly at right angles with the trunk. But the posture which is temporarily assumed by the primitive tree-climber is very different from this, for in the interval which we are picturing its body axis is tending to become carried upright upon a thigh which is more or less extended as the trunk is raised towards the grasping hands. It is tree-climbing which makes this posture a possibility, and even its temporary adoption marks a great step in evolution, since, with the increasing perfection of the arboreal activities, the assumption of this posture is an oft-recurring one.

With the repetition of this action anatomical changes are brought about in the limb, for many adaptations must take place when the femur is brought into line with the vertebral axis instead of being at right angles to it. These adaptations will show their first manifestations even when the demand for the posture is only occasional. Briefly, the femur becomes capable of a more complete rotation at the hip-joint, so that its extension may be carried through a right angle, and it may take up a position parallel to the axis of the vertebral column.

The capsule of the joint becomes modified to permit of this extension, and the muscles become accommodated to the new poise. In the completely adapted arboreal animal this posture tends to become more or less habitual. In some of the Lemurs it is almost as well established as in the Anthropoids themselves, and under these conditions the anatomical adaptations become more perfect. The fibres of the capsule of the hip-joint take on a permanent twist, such as is seen to perfection in the capsule of the human hip-joint (see Fig. 22), and the muscles (*e.g.*, the M. rectus femoris) dispose themselves to the best mechanical advantage for performing the movements of the joint.

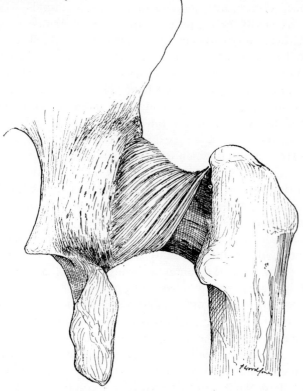

Fig. 22.—The Human Hip-Joint from Behind, to show Twisting of the Fibres of the Capsule of the Joint.

When the leg has become rotated backwards, and the muscles and joints have adapted themselves to this change, there still has to be an elaboration of the supporting mechanism in this new position. These forces are all in action during arboreal life, but they gain an added importance in the habitual orthograde posture of Man.

The trunk is first suspended upright from the arms upon the extended legs (as in the existing Gibbons) (see Fig. 23), next its weight is partially borne upon the extended legs (as in the existing Giant Apes), afterwards it is entirely borne and balanced upon the fully extended legs in all the ordinary activities of the animal (as in Man).

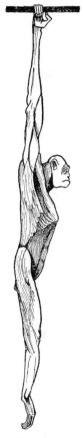

The anatomical adaptations which accompany these changes, as they are seen in existing Primates, are practically continuous and harmonious; but this is not equivalent to saying that the evolution of the process is seen in progress among existing types.

In Man, the fascial insertion and the great increase in size of the M. gluteus maximus, the extended fascial insertions of other leg muscles, the modifications of the calf muscles (M. gastrocnemius and M. soleus), and, above all, the development of the M. peroneus tertius, are all instances of the specializations of muscles for the balancing of an upright body upon an extended leg.

These are later changes produced by terrestrial bipedal orthograde habits, in which the suspending assistance of the hands is entirely dispensed with, but all these things had their beginnings in purely arboreal life.

Only one other change we need notice here, and that is the finishing touch of the eversion of the foot in Man. When the arboreal hind-limb has been perfected as a supporting organ in an extended position, it is still a purely

Fig. 23.—Diagram of a Gibbon (*Hylobates lar*) suspended by the grasp of its hands.

From a drawing made from a photograph by Prof. Arthur Keith.

5

arboreal grasping-supporting limb. As such, its third segment is still fitted for application to the branches upon the grasp of which its powers of support depend. In conformity with this, its sole is inturned, so that it may be applied to the rounded sides of the branches along which the animal walks. The higher Apes and primitive Man climb up branches with the big toe separated from the other toes, so that the outer side of the foot tends to be applied to one side of the branch, whilst the big toe grasps the other side. In this method of progression the foot is inverted, the soles look inwards, from opposite sides of the branch, towards each other. When the branches are exchanged for the level surface of the earth, this inversion of the foot is a useful adaptation no longer, and in terrestrial bipedal progression a new mechanism is initiated for the eversion of the foot. Into these changes—which are peculiarly human—it is impossible to enter, since they are all finishing touches added after the arboreal habit was abandoned. The eversion of the foot of Man is a post-arboreal development, so also is the perfected mechanism for balancing the trunk upon the extended leg; but the extension of the leg upon the trunk, and the anatomical adaptations it involved, are pure outcomes of the ordinary evolution of the arboreal habit.

CHAPTER XII

THUMBS AND BIG TOES

So far, we have, in considering the question of the development of the grasp, dealt only with the power of (1) adapting the palmar surface of the hand and foot to the branch, and (2) flexing the fingers over it, to make the adaptation more perfect. For the perfected grasp another factor comes in, since the hold is made more secure by folding digits over both sides of the object to be grasped. This simple requirement has led to the most divergent developments, when the climbing Vertebrates are looked at as a whole. Among the existing Reptiles, the Chameleons show the most extreme development of arboreal grasp, and in them the fourth and fifth digits are turned directly backwards, away from the third, second and first, which retain their primitive forward direction.

In the perching Birds, some variety exists in the arrangement of the clasping digits; and the so-called Zygodactyle foot of the Scansores achieves the same effect as is attained by the Chameleon.

In the Mammals, and especially among the Primate stock, the arboreal life has led to the specialization of one digit upon hand and foot, which opposes the remaining four digits. These opposing digits are the thumb (pollex) and the big toe (hallux). By an opposing digit we mean one that can be turned round so that its palmar aspect is opposed to the palmar aspect of the remaining digits, and therefore can be placed, for example, upon the opposite side of a branch.

The subjects of thumbs and big toes has provided an

arena in which anatomists, philosophers, and even divines have met and done battle. Man has a well-developed thumb, which is opposable to the remaining fingers. He has a big toe, which is well developed, but which is not opposable to his other toes. The human thumb has received excessive praise from philosophers, the big toe has also come in for its share, but upon the question of the homology of the hallux and pollex there is the widest difference of opinion. Arguments upon the question have been carried to extremes. " I have heard a distinguished naturalist say to a class that he would stake anything, short of his eternal salvation, that the thumb corresponds to the little toe, and the little finger to the great toe, and that he should think his life well spent in establishing the doctrine " (Dwight).

We need not be led aside into any such controversies, for it does not matter to us if the thumb finds its strict serial homologue in the little toe or in the big toe; it is quite certain that in the latter it finds its exact functional equivalent. By way of homology we will be quite satisfied with the simple fact that, in the mammalian position of the limbs, *it is the digit which is situated nearest the middle line of the body that is specialized as the opposing digit.* This power to oppose one digit to the remaining members of the series is no part of the heritage of the primitive•third segment of the limb; it is a new development called forth by the increasing perfection and the increasing needs of the power to grasp. The mere anatomical arrangement by which opposition may be produced among the digits is no necessary part of the characteristics of the Primates, nor is it alone within their phylum that it is displayed. Some of the very thoroughly arboreal Marsupials have perfected this arrangement, and most of the Phalangers possess an opposable big toe. Even developments such as are seen in the Chameleon, among the Reptiles, and in the Parrots, among Birds, are hinted at in the hand of the Koala (*Phascolarctus*), in which the two inner digits tend to be separated from, and opposed to, the outer three. Certain arboreal Rodents have developed very perfectly opposable thumbs and big toes upon lines exactly similar to the Primates, and this feature is seen very beautifully in an arboreal mouse (*Mus margarettæ*) discovered by Charles Hose in Borneo.

Within the Primate phylum some very curious irregularities are apparent in the distribution of the power of opposing thumbs and big toes among the scattered living types. It seems strange that no New-World monkey possesses a perfectly opposable thumb, although all possess an opposable big toe. Among the New-World Primates the thumb is not perfectly opposable, and is always permanently in line with the rest of the digits; it tends to be small and unimportant, and may be entirely undeveloped.

At first sight it might seem that this arrangement was correlated with the development of a prehensile tail, but all the American Primates are not prehensile-tailed. Nevertheless, it is not beyond possibility that some functional factor may have been the common cause for both developments; a common factor may have led to the loss, or non-development, of the opposable thumb and to the perfection of the prehensile tail, but these two features need not occur in combination. This I regard as the most probable explanation, and in the actual method of climbing characteristic of different groups the origin of the different developments probably lies.

The little Marmosets (*Hapalidæ*), which have claws instead of nails upon all the digits save the big toe, possess a well-developed, but not opposable, thumb. In the *Cebidæ* the condition varies. The Howling Monkeys (*Mycetes*) possess well-developed thumbs, prehensile tails, and the usual opposable big toes. The Sakis (*Pitheciæ*) have well-developed thumbs, but the tail is not prehensile; the Night Monkeys (*Nyctipithecus*) show the same features. In the prehensile-tailed Spider Monkeys (*Ateles*) the thumb is rudimentary or absent, while the Woolly Monkeys (*Lagothrix*) possess a thumb. The Capuchins of the typical genus *Cebus* possess a well-developed thumb and a tail, which, though partially prehensile, is not so specialized as that of *Ateles* or *Lagothrix*.

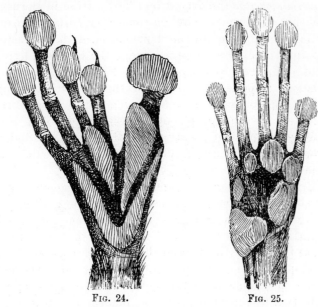

FIG. 24.   FIG. 25.

FIG. 24.—PLANTAR SURFACE OF THE RIGHT FOOT OF *Tarsius Spectrum*, SHOWING THE PECULIAR DEVELOPMENT OF THE BIG TOE.

FIG 25.—PALMAR SURFACE OF THE RIGHT HAND OF *Tarsius Spectrum*.

In all the Old-World Primates the pollex, when present, is opposable. In the Lemurs the big toe is opposable and is often extremely specialized, the hallux standing apart from the foot in some species, such as *Tarsius spectrum*, in a manner reminiscent of the split foot of some of the arboreal members of lower orders (Fig. 24). The thumb is also well developed and opposable in most higher or typical Lemurs (see Fig. 25). In the Asiatic

monkeys of the genus *Semnopithecus*, which includes the
sacred Langurs, the thumb is small but still opposable,
and in the allied African genus *Colubus* it is reduced to a
mere tubercle, or is altogether absent. The well-developed
big toe is present in all (see Fig. 26). In the Anthropoids,
as a rule, the thumb and the big toe are well developed
and opposable.

We may therefore say that among the scattered and
very diverse living members of the Primates the development of the thumb and big toe shows
both from the point of view of mere size,
and as opposable digits, some striking
irregularities. But it is not to be
doubted that the underlying principle
is clear enough, that the arboreal habit
develops the specialized and opposable
thumb and big toe, and that peculiar
habits of climbing account for the actual
condition present in the hand and foot
of any individual species. A freakish
development of tree-climbing, or an
overdoing of the pure ability to climb,
may lead to secondary specializations
away from the simple condition. The
stock from which Man has sprung
shows in this, as in so many other
features, a tempered adaptation to the
arboreal habit without the development
of any secondary specializations.

FIG. 26. — THE
LEFT FOOT OF
*Macacus Nemes-
trinus* AS SEEN
FROM ITS PLAN-
TAR ASPECT.

We may imagine that, from some
early stage in which both thumb and
big toe were equally specialized for pre-
hension, the human stock cultivated especially the hand
as the grasping organ, and so retained and perfected the
opposable thumb. Some other members of the Primate
stock depended more upon the grasp of the foot, and so
have retained and specialized an opposable big toe, at

times even to the extent of suppressing the development of the thumb. Some have also called in the tail to assist in the foot grasp, and further deprived the hand and thumb of their function of suspending the body in climbing.

We see in this feature a correlated adaptation to the climbing habit to which I have previously drawn attention; those Primates which show a tendency to depend on foot grasp descend a tree head foremost, and those which depend upon hand grasp walk down feet first. The human stock walked down, and converted the opposable big toe into a remarkably useful supporting big toe.

The human thumb is an arboreal grasping organ, perfected by ancestors which depended upon their hand grasp in their arboreal activities. The human big toe is nothing more than a modified arboreal grasping organ, the primitive characters of which were stamped upon it by its specialization as a grasping organ, which supported the weight of the body in climbing.

We must not overlook the fact that although the grasping power of the big toe is largely lost in modern Europeans, it must still be reckoned as a distinctly human possession. Kohlbrugge has remarked that one would hardly dare to suggest that the presence of a prehensile big toe was a sign of human inferiority, were the discussion to take place at an anthropological congress held in Tokio. In the very primitive negrito races the power of foot grasp is well retained. For the purposes of petty theft the Sakai largely relies on the grasp of his toes (Skeat and Blagden); and very many other instances could be furnished from races far more highly placed in the human scale.

CHAPTER XIII

THE HUMAN FOOT

THE human hand, a strangely, almost shockingly, primitive survival, has received enormous praise mistakenly lavished by the philosopher and the anatomist; but the human foot, a wonderfully modified and distinctly human member, has had but scant appreciation. This assertion is made in the face of the fact that the human foot has provided the subject-matter for monographs in several languages.

The foot is apt to be regarded as a poor relation of the hand, as a thing which, once being far more useful, has degenerated, within the narrow confines of a boot, into a rather distorted and somewhat useless member. Although in modern Man the boot has had its definite influence (as in limiting the possibilities of the power of grasp), such generalizations concerning the human foot are very far from true. If Man should wish to point with pride to any organ the structure of which definitely severs him from all other existing Primates, it is to the foot that he should point. If "missing links" are to be tracked with complete success, the foot, far more than the skull, or the teeth, or the shins, will mark them as Monkey or as Man. The weakness of Achilles lay in his heel; the weakness of the arboreal Primate masquerading as Man lies in the structure of its foot.

It is in the grades of evolution of the foot that the stages of the missing link will be most plainly presented to the future paleontologist, when time and chance shall have discovered the feet of such forms as *Pithecanthropus* and *Eoanthropus*.

There was a period in zoological literature when discussion was waged earnestly, and without satisfaction, as to what should be called a hand and what a foot. The hand and the foot are alike in some animals; they are quadrupedal or quadrumanous, but some exhibit differences in the structure of the third segment of the fore and hind limbs. The point in dispute was the exact stage at which differentiation in a quadrumanous animal produced a hand and a foot. In this academic discussion Etienne Geoffroy St. Hillaire, Huxley, Owen, and many others took their part. We may say, however, that the problem as it was presented did not offer any very special difficulty beyond the determination of the function of the member. This was the solution which Huxley recognized at once, and to which he always adhered. The Anthropoids have hands and feet, and their hands and feet are differentiated by their function. We will accept such a solution, and assume that we understand perfectly well what we mean when we speak of a Gorilla's foot. That is a simple way out of the dilemma, but we must recognize it does not do away with the difficulty which presents itself the moment we attempt to differentiate between a hand and a foot from the point of view of structure. A monkey's foot is a definite thing; it has a definite function which distinguishes it from the hand (see Fig. 27). The same applies with even more force to the case of an Anthropoid, but the hand and foot in these animals are, anatomically, remarkably similar structures in many ways. The specialization of the foot as a supporting organ is carried to very definite lengths in the Anthropoids; in the Gorilla is seen the best foot developed among the Giant Apes. We will therefore take this foot as an anatomical illustration of the stage of development to which foot differentiation is carried in existing Primates. The foot of a Gorilla differs from the hand in the fact that all the digits are placed nearer to the extremity of the third segment of the hind limb; there is a greater length of foot behind the base of the great toe than there is of hand behind the base of the thumb (see Fig. 28).

This posterior elongation of the foot or development of a heel is present also in many monkeys. The big toe of the Gorilla is larger and better developed than the

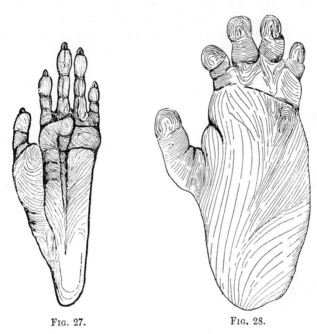

FIG. 27.   FIG. 28.

FIG. 27.—THE LEFT FOOT OF *Cercopithecus palatinus* SEEN FROM ITS PLANTAR ASPECT.

FIG. 28.—PLANTAR SURFACE OF THE LEFT FOOT OF A YOUNG GORILLA.

With details of the cutaneous markings, after Duckworth, from a specimen in the Cambridge Collection.

thumb; the remaining toes are not so well developed as the corresponding fingers; nevertheless, they retain exactly the same relative proportions. We may speak of a digital formula for hand and foot, such a formula being an expression of the relative degree of projection of the digits. In the Gorilla, the digital formula for the foot is exactly the same as that for the hand, and both may be expressed as: $3>4>2>5>1$. Such a formula is an exceedingly primitive one, and it is present in the primitive manus of such chelonian reptiles as the water tortoises. The strangely primitive human hand has an identical digital formula, the third being the finger that reaches farthest forwards, the fourth the next, the second the next, followed by the fifth, and the thumb is farthest back of all. There is an almost equally common variation in the human hand in which the second digit may be as long as, or longer than, the fourth, and this is doubtless due to the functional importance of the index-finger. I am not sure that it should not be considered as the typical human condition. In such cases the formula stands thus: $3>2>4>5>1$, or $3>2=4>5>1$.

Man retains a very primitive digital formula for his hand. His nearest Primate kinsfolk retain it for both hands and feet.

It is when we attempt to apply this formula to the human foot that we see how great is the alteration that has taken place between the existing Anthropoid with the best primate foot and Man himself. The digital formula for the human foot is as a rule: $1>2>3>4>5$ (see Figs. 29 and 30). Such a statement holds good for the feet of the great majority of present-day British people. It is commonly assumed by artists, and even by surgeons, that the elongated big toe which projects in advance of the other four toes is not a natural human characteristic, but is a result of boot pressure. A long big toe is regarded rather as a deformity than as a natural human possession in which to take justifiable pride.

Professor Flower long ago turned his attention to this point, and he examined the feet of hundreds of the bare-footed children of Perthshire, and among them all he found no case in which the big toe did not project beyond the second toe. We must look upon a big toe which

dominates the whole series as a typically human and a
perfectly natural feature. Nevertheless, it is common
enough to see feet in which the second toe is longer than
the big toe. People who have feet with such a digital
formula are apt to be somewhat proud of the fact, for

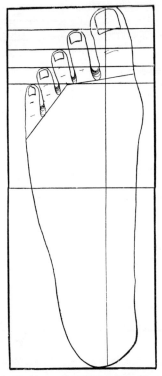

FIG. 29.—TYPE OF FOOT IN WHICH THE BIG TOE IS CONSIDERABLY
LONGER THAN ANY OF THE OTHER TOES, WHICH DIMINISH
IN REGULAR SEQUENCE FROM FIRST TO FIFTH.

Traced from the outline of the foot.

such a foot is supposed to conform to the " Greek ideal,"
but that this type of foot ever was the ideal of Greek
artists is disputed by some authorities upon the subject,
and certainly we may assume that it is less typically
human, and more ape-like, than the type of foot of the
average hospital patient who possesses a long big toe

(see Fig. 31). So far we have as the typical digital formula for the human foot $1>2>3>4>5$, with a not uncommon variant $2>1>3>4>5$. There is yet another type, which seems much less common, in which $2=3>1$ $>4>5$. In the Museum of the Royal College of Surgeons is the skeleton of a Bushman, in which it is possible that

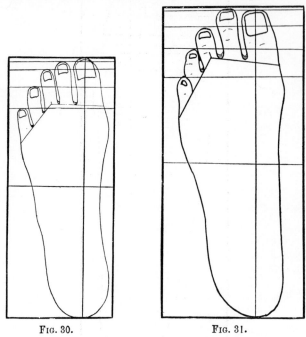

FIG. 30. FIG. 31.

FIG. 30.—OUTLINE OF A CHILD'S FOOT.

FIG. 31.—OUTLINE OF A FOOT IN WHICH THE SECOND TOE IS LONGER THAN THE BIG TOE. THE SO-CALLED GREEK IDEAL.

the third digit was longest of all—a distinctly anthropoid condition. The change from the so-called Greek ideal to the foot with the dominant big toe is almost certainly no outcome of boot-wearing, nor is any one link in the whole sequence of the atrophy of the fifth, fourth, third, and second digits. All are natural processes of evolution, and all have probably taken place in a series of missing

Zoologically speaking, we may say that the very useful and specialized foot adapted for terrestrial progression is a foot of few digits. It may, in fact, be a foot composed of a solitary digit. The evolutionary stages by which the horse has come to stand solely upon its third digit are well known. Similar processes produced the two-digited foot of the deer and of the ostrich. There can be no doubt that Man is trusting, not to his third digit, but to his first, and all the others are undergoing a process of comparative atrophy. This is in reality a most interesting problem. There is an admitted tendency to specialize one digit in a thoroughly adapted terrestrial foot. Man applied an arboreal foot to terrestrial progression, and in this arboreal foot the best-developed member was the old grasping digit—the first or big toe. It seems that upon taking to a terrestrial life he has started the elaboration of this already specialized toe, and is tending towards the development of a foot which is quite unique—a foot in which the first digit is the dominant, and in the end, perhaps, the sole surviving, member.

It needs no special demonstration to make plain the fact that the little toe is somewhat of a rudiment in most Europeans. Usually it is but a poor thing; its nail is ill developed, and at times no nail is present. It is particularly liable to that circulatory disturbance which manifests itself in chilblains, and not uncommonly it seems in a poor state of nutrition. Most people possess but little power of movement in it, and its skeleton shows that its atrophic condition has affected the bones and joints, for the last two phalanges are very commonly fused together, making it short of a joint as compared with the rest of the toes. Very commonly its axis is not straight, and the toe is humped up and also somewhat bent laterally.

It is easy to assume that all this is merely the result of wearing boots, but it is perfectly certain that this common explanation is not the correct one.

In many races, the members of which are quite innocent of wearing boots at any period of their lives, the little toe is just as atrophic as it is in the average London hospital patient, and in some unbooted native races it is even more degenerated than is common in the booted Londoner. Among the Malays, the absence of a nail upon the remarkably stumpy fifth toe is not at all uncommon. The barefooted races in Nubia are no better off in this matter, and even in the very primitive Sakai the little toe has suffered.

Vaughan Stevens has noted that the little toe of the Sakai is not straight, but is " bent like ours," and is small in proportion; but the Jakuns, according to the same authority, have little toes which are straight (Skeat and Blagden).

I imagine that just as the big toe is becoming the dominant toe, the little toe is becoming a rudiment, and I presume that, in their turn, the fourth, third, and second toes are undergoing a human evolutionary atrophy. There is a most interesting anatomical feature which is explained by this trend of human foot development.

In the hand a system of short muscles, which serves to part the fingers and close them together (M. interosseii), is ranged symmetrically upon either side of the third or middle digit. This digit therefore constitutes the middle line of the hand from which, and to which, the other fingers can be moved laterally.

In the Monkeys, with the digital formula of the foot similar to that of the hand, a like grouping of muscles is seen about the third toe, which in movements, as well as in length and axis, constitutes the middle line digit of the foot.

The same condition is seen in the Chimpanzee and Orang-utan. In Man, however, the muscle symmetry is ranged about the second digit, and to and from this second digit the other toes are moved laterally. The middle line of the human foot has changed from the third to the second toe. In the Gorilla, a most interesting phase is seen, for while in most specimens the middle line of the foot passes through the third toe, " it must be admitted that many Gorillas possess the human arrangement, these muscles being grouped about an axis formed by the second digit " (Duckworth).

When digits atrophy and disappear in phylogeny, it seems to be the rule that their reduction starts from their distal extremities; the terminal phalanx diminishes first, and the metacarpal is only affected at a much later period in evolution. Metacarpal bones of absent digits persist, as the well-known splint bones of the horse. It is to be expected that the same order should be followed in the diminishing toes of the outer side of the human foot. The terminal phalanx of the fifth toe is commonly a rudiment, and often it is fused to the next phalanx, of which bone it then constitutes a mere distal tubercle. Compared with the fingers, there has been a great reduction in the terminal phalanges of all the toes except the big toe, and the two basal phalanges are diminished in a somewhat lesser degree. In the majority of cases, however, the metacarpal bones have not suffered any very marked atrophy, and the metacarpal formula is often that which should exist for the primitive digits. Much individual variation is seen in the skeletons of different feet, but the metacarpal bone of the big toe is, at times, shorter than that of the second, which in its turn is shorter than the third; the fourth, again, is shorter than the third, and the fifth shorter than the fourth.

One very curious evidence of this skeletal condition is seen in very many feet, even when the big toe is far in advance of all the rest. Although a line joining the tips of the toes slopes without interruption from the first to the fifth, a line joining the bases of these toes does not follow the same course. From the first cleft it rises to the second, and from the fourth cleft it rises to the third, and there is thus produced a sharp angle in the line which

6

usually falls opposite the middle of the base of the third digit (see Figs. 29, 30 and 31). This line has exactly the same contour in the hand, and is the typical one seen in the Monkey's foot. It is the outline of the primitive foot preserved in its primitive condition by arboreal life. The contour of the anterior extremity of the human foot has therefore not undergone much change from its primitive arboreal condition, the alteration being almost solely confined to the phalanges of the free digits.

It is the outer toes which are undergoing atrophy, and this atrophy has not to any great extent affected the metacarpal bones, nor altered the outline of the foot itself.

Human specializations seem to be producing a tendency to depend upon, and develop especially as supporting organs, the bones of the inner margin of the foot. The big toe and its supporting bones are becoming the principal axis of the foot.

The imperfect efforts at walking upon the feet which the higher Primates can make have not attained to this human development. The human baby walks upon the outer side of its feet when it first learns to walk, and the bones upon this side of the foot are the first to become ossified. But a typically human and later change is the eversion of the foot, which brings its inner margin into the line transmitting the weight of the body to the ground. A whole series of finishing touches in human development is brought into play in this process, but since they are essentially not arboreal effects, they cannot be dealt with here.

However, without going into the details of the eversion of the foot, the general facts are clear enough. Man has inherited a primitive and arboreal foot; purely human modifications are obviously at work producing a very typical human type of structure which, adapted in the first place for support in an arboreal habitat, is now being fitted for terrestrial progression. The human foot is a definite human evolution, and some may take comfort in remembering that it is evidence of a high grade of human evolution to possess a long big toe accompanied by a steadily diminishing series of toes towards the outer side of the foot, and that it is not necessary to label as " sensible " the person, or the fashion, which seeks to confine this human foot into a boot constructed for the digital formula of an arboreal Primate.

CHAPTER XIV

THE RECESSION OF THE SNOUT REGION

WE have seen that one of the things made possible by
the emancipation of the fore-limb and the development
of the power of grasp is the ability of the animal to seize
its food with its hand and convey it to its mouth. These
are two separate actions, and although their influence is
exerted in the same direction, they are so distinct as to
need somewhat separate treatment. The perfected combination of these actions doubtless came slowly into the
arboreal stock, but the power to seize food with the hands
is present in some quite lowly forms, and the Tree Shrews
(*Tupaiadæ*) already possess the power of raising food to
their mouths. In all the Lemurs these actions are
perfected, and passing over the degrees to which they are
developed in different species, we will study the completed
process as seen in a typical Primate, and note what
correlated changes may be bound up in its full development.

We must first turn aside to note that there are other
animals than the Primates and their kindred which can
grasp food in their hands and convey it to their mouths.
There are even animals showing no trace of being arboreal
which can do this action with great address. It is the
same with all systems and organs, and it is a story to
which we shall repeatedly have to turn, for, as we have
seen, the fore-limb may receive some degree of emancipation by other activities than tree-climbing. Jumping
and hopping animals, and animals which sit upright, can
use their hands for many skilled movements. Jerboas

(*Dipodinæ*), and many other hopping Rodents, eat food held between their fore-paws. Beavers can hold a small object clasped by the palm and claws of one hand, and Marmots (*Arctomys*) even go farther than this, for when sitting erect they can pick up their food from the ground. Truly arboreal animals of other stocks again possess this power, and squirrels, phalangers, and opossums are good examples of limited hand-feeding arboreal types. So far as the process goes in any of these animals, the changes which we are picturing in the Primate stock take · place harmoniously.

A typical Primate obtains its food with its hand instead of adopting the common mammalian method of taking it with its mouth: one function of the mouth, that of food-getting, is therefore relegated to the hand in the Primates.

It may be said on broad lines that throughout the whole of the animal kingdom the mouth parts show a development depending upon the nature of the animal's food and the method of taking it. If it is the hand which becomes the grasping organ, the mouth and the anatomical structures connected with it need no longer be developed in any special way to carry on this function. The food-grasping power of the Primate hand renders unnecessary the development of grasping lips and a long series of grasping teeth. Again, the fact that the food once grasped by the hand is conveyed by the hand to the mouth renders the mouth and its associated parts merely an organ for dealing with food already grasped and carried to it. A mouth merely adapted for the reception of food already grasped and brought to it is a structure very different from a mouth adapted for the purposes of reaching out for food, seizing the food so reached, and subsequently dealing with it.

When the mouth is the food-obtaining organ, there is a necessity for its situation being advanced from the face, and especially that part of the face in which the eyes are

situated. A long snout with a mouth opening far in
advance of the eyes is a necessity in any animal which
uses its mouth alone, in all the processes of obtaining
food. The grazing herbivores must carry their food-
getting mouth far in advance of their eyes. The long
face of the horse may serve as a familiar example. The
animals which catch insects must have a similar structure,
and the " snouty " insectivorous Shrews are typical of
such animals. The more the fore-limbs serve to obtain
or to hold the food, the less is this snout developed, and
I am terming the change which hand-feeding produces
the recession of the snout region. In herbivorous animals
the transition is very easily seen; the long-faced horse
may be contrasted (solely from the point of view of this
function) with the short-faced squirrel which holds food
between its fore-paws. In carnivorous animals and mixed
feeders another factor comes in, for the mouth may be
used, not only for grasping, but for killing the food, or
the fore-limb may take over this function in part.

The long-faced dog grasps and kills its food with its
mouth, the shorter-faced cat holds its food with its fore-
paws and kills either with its paws or with its mouth;
but the tiger, in which the snout region has shortened
very considerably, kills as a rule with its fore-limb, and
holds the kill with its paws. I have noticed, in this
respect, some interesting phases among the Primate stock.
I had at the same time, living as nearly as possible in
their natural state, some Lemurs (*Nycticebus tardigradus*)
and some Monkeys. Both of these animals, although
mixed feeders, are in a state of nature very fond of animal
food, the Lemur delighting in insects, especially grass-
hoppers, and young birds, the monkey always ready to
kill and eat anything, from a cockroach to a chicken.

The Lemur would catch a grasshopper with its
hand (or its foot), and would catch a bird put into its
cage in exactly the same way, but after a preliminary
squeezing would almost invariably put it to its mouth to

kill it with its teeth. I have seen *Nycticebus* tear grass-
hoppers to pieces with its hands, but birds it always
killed by biting. The monkeys were adepts at catching
birds, and although chained they had no difficulty in
seizing the confiding Java sparrows that were attracted
by their food. The bird was caught in one hand, and
was then killed by being pulled and twisted between the
two hands. Generally the monkey wrung the bird's neck
so thoroughly that it succeeded in pulling it altogether
apart; it killed with its hands, and then conveyed the
kill to its mouth with its hands.

In the Primates, owing to the preponderant use of the
fore-limb, there is no need for a mouth which reaches out
for food, or for a mouth which seizes food or kills it when
seized, all these functions being discharged by the mobile
and grasping fore-limb.

Now teeth are developed for different purposes. They
are developed for cutting herbage, for seizing animal
food, and for killing prey as well as for biting it up pre-
paratory to swallowing. Some teeth subserve the function of obtaining a variety of food in a variety of ways,
and some subserve the function of preparing this food for
the processes of digestion. With the adaptation of the
hand for obtaining food, the need for the specialization
of teeth for this purpose will no longer be felt so strongly,
and it is natural to suppose that the tooth series will
become abbreviated, only those teeth which are necessary
for dealing with food brought to them by the hand
remaining fully functional. We may assume, as a ground-
plan of the mammalian tooth series, an upper and a lower
set, composed of three incisors, one canine, four pre-
molars, and three molars upon each side of the jaw.
Such a tooth series comprises forty-four teeth, and it
is seen, for example, in the elongated jaws of the
omnivorous pig.

If we trace this tooth series through the Primates and
their probable next of kin, we find the full forty-four in

the terrestrial Insectivora.   In the arboreal Tree Shrews
(*Tupaiadæ*) it has become reduced to thirty-eight by the
loss of one upper incisor and an upper and lower premolar upon each side.   In the Lemurs only thirty-six
teeth remain, for a corresponding lower incisor has been
lost.   In the Old-World Monkeys, the Anthropoid Apes,
and Man, one more premolar is lost in each jaw upon
either side, and the dentition is reduced to a set of thirty-
two teeth.   In Man there are signs of a further reduction.

The reduction of the tooth series and the shortening of
the jaw in the arboreal stock go on step by step together,
and for the same reason, and yet to a certain extent the
two developments are independent of each other.   The
tooth series may diminish and may even disappear, yet
if food is still reached for and is seized by the mouth the
snout region will remain elongated.   A toothless animal
may still be a long-jawed animal if long jaws are needed
to take food which when taken requires no teeth for its
killing or for its mastication.   With hand-feeding the
recession of the snout may outstrip the reduction of the
tooth series, and this process is evidenced in the stock
we are considering.   Starting with a full mammalian
series of forty-four teeth, the snout region may yet be so
long that gaps exist between the teeth, and different
groups of teeth may be widely separated from each other.
Reduction in the tooth series in this stock does not increase the gaps, but the gaps diminish faster than the
tooth series is reduced.   The ultimate result of this
process is that Man, with a reduced number of teeth,
has the most crowded dentition.   Man is the only living
Primate that has its teeth arranged in a continuous series,
and it is one of his distinctions that there are no gaps
between them.   The process of the shortening of the
snout, outstripping the process of reduction of the dental
series, gives rise to one of the great problems of modern
dentistry—the proper treatment of the many evils arising
from overcrowded jaws.   To this subject we will turn

again, but we can here sum up the last phases of the process by saying that if primitive and natural Man has no gaps between his adult teeth, his children always have gaps between the smaller teeth of their first set; but the children of modern and civilized Man are losing even these gaps with the shortening of the jaws.

CHAPTER XV

THE RECESSION OF THE JAWS AND REDUCTION OF THE TOOTH SERIES

WITH the business of hand-feeding, Man has gone a great deal farther than any other member of the Primates, and that comparatively modern development—civilized Man—has gone still farther. The highest Primates select their food with their hands, they even do more than this, for, to a certain extent, they prepare it for eating with their hands. But this preparation, though an enormous stride, does not go to very great lengths beyond peeling a banana or husking a thin-shelled nut with the fingers; for anything much more exacting the teeth are requisitioned. We have seen the amount of work that the hands have already saved the teeth in the evolution of an arboreal stock, and there is obviously a tendency in the highest apes for the hands to assume further duties. Man has applied his brain and his mobile hands more fully to this problem, and he has saved his teeth to the utmost limits, but has made a sorry bargain. The general bearing of these factors did not escape the notice of Darwin, but, strangely enough, he confined his argument practically to the fact that the hands of the human ancestors, armed with primitive weapons, tended to take the place of the fighting canine teeth. " As they gradually acquired the habit of using stones, clubs, and other weapons, for fighting with their enemies, they would have used their jaws and teeth less and less. In this case, the jaws, together with the teeth, would have become reduced in size, as we may feel sure from innumerable analogous cases." In many ways, therefore, human hands have replaced the functions of human teeth. There is no need to trace the stages in a story familiar to all. Man has ground, husked, prepared, cleaned, and finally cooked his food. He has freed it from hard parts, and made it " tender " in every conceivable way. His canine teeth he has replaced by the use of his hands; his flint or his knife has usurped the function of his incisors; and his molars he has relegated to the kitchen premises as a pestle and mortar in some form or other. Even when he had done all this he had not run the whole gamut of robbing his teeth and jaws of their legitimate occupation, for there is still the knife and fork of the Europeanized to perform outside the mouth those duties formerly performed within it.

Every organ which loses its function must undergo a change, and unless this change leads to the assumption of new functions, the ultimate result will be an atrophy of that organ. The human teeth, deprived in great measure of their normal functions, acquire no new ones—even speaking and whistling through the teeth may not save them from their ultimate destiny—and it is not to be denied that, slowly, of course, but still surely, they are undergoing atrophy. Among existing races of mankind the fact is patent, the observation is a commonplace of anthropology. " The possession of an ample palate and large well-formed teeth by the black races is a matter of common knowledge (as is the fact that in the crania of the prehistoric inhabitants of Europe the size and quality of the teeth were superior to those at present obtaining in the same geographical area). It is therefore impossible to overlook the inference that reduction in the size of the teeth is at least attendant (if not dependent) upon the acquisition of higher grades of civilization and directly upon diet and the preparation of food."

This, from the writings of Dr. Duckworth, may be taken as an orthodox statement of the general position as summed up in modern anthropology. The more primitive races have larger and better formed teeth, rooted in more roomy palates, than members of more civilized races can boast of. There is but little need to dilate upon so well known a circumstance, but some few facts may be cited.

The third molars, wisdom teeth, being the last to be erupted in the already diminished jaws, show the maximum effects of the atrophic influences of disuse. In modern civilized Man these teeth are erupted late, frequently in a condition of defective development, and usually in such a manner as to restrict, if not entirely to obviate, their functional utility. In civilized Man they are always smaller than the first or second molars, and as a rule all their biting cusps are not fully developed. They may not all be erupted; sometimes they are present in one jaw, and not in the other, and often when present in both jaws they do not meet and bite together. Frequently they altogether fail to be erupted.

In primitive races they are rarely absent, they are cut earlier, and are but little if any smaller than the other molars, and they bite and grind together in a perfectly even manner.

In the skulls of the ancient inhabitants of Egypt and Nubia this perfection of the third molars is very striking. Among the modern Egyptians—even those of them leading a town life in Cairo—the wisdom teeth are cut at times well before the eighteenth year—full six years before they make their imperfect appearance in most Europeans. In the more primitive living races the third molars are usually very fine teeth, erupted early, and fully capable of all the typical molar-grinding functions. In the skulls of the earliest human remains in which the dental series is preserved, the molar teeth are large, and the molar series diminishes little, if at all, from the first to the third molar; indeed, in some cases the primitive condition of a reversed state of affairs is seen, and the third molar is larger than the second, which in turn is larger than the first. In modern Man the first molar is markedly larger than the second, which is again markedly larger than the third. In the higher Apes the third molar is the largest tooth of the molar series, and it erupts before the canine. There is one other circum-stance connected with the molar teeth that is worthy of note. It is not extremely rare for a fourth molar tooth to be developed in the roomy jaws of the skulls of ancient races, and it is not at all uncommon for some diminished remnant of this tooth to be present in modern primitive Man. The presence of this fourth molar is all the more remarkable, since its normal presence has to be sought in a stock so apparently remote as the metatherian (Marsupial) Mammals.

Apart altogether from the anatomical development of individual teeth, some light is thrown upon this question by studying the quality of the teeth when developed. We know that the teeth readily decay, and that caries in modern civilized man affects the permanent set of the adult and the temporary set of the child. Caries of the milk teeth is so common as to be the rule in modern city children, and few children shed their milk teeth without decay having played some havoc among a set of teeth the normal functional life of which is naturally brief. But although the milk teeth were not intended to remain in functional activity for more than ten years, they were not meant to decay before or at that time. It is a striking fact that, in the work of the Archæological Survey of Nubia (1907-08), no case of caries of the milk teeth was found in the skull of any child living before the dawn of the Christian era in Nubia. Among the hundreds of cases examined, not one case of caries of the milk denti-tion was discovered in the children of the early Egyptians. The children of the more primitive living races rarely show any traces of decay in the teeth of their infantile set. In modern civilized children living a city life, not only is caries of the milk teeth almost the rule, but dental surgeons commonly " stop " milk teeth nowadays, so early is the onset of their decay. The decay of the permanent teeth needs no description, its almost universal occurrence in civilized modern man being familiar to all. But remarkably good sets of permanent teeth are found in skulls of historical date, and in the remains of ancient races extensive caries of the permanent teeth becomes increasingly rare. One definite factor has certainly played a large part in this deterioration of the teeth of modern Man, and this factor is the loss of the reaction to wear and tear—the loss of the power of repair.

When a horse grinds its molars together it wears them down, and the enamel with which the surfaces of the cusps are covered is worn off, and the main substance of the tooth (dentine) is exposed below. Year after year the cusps are worn flatter, and an ever-changing pattern is produced, the pattern being made by areas of exposed dentine surrounded by margins of enamel. The dentine which is exposed in this way reacts to the grinding influences, and becomes hardened on its surface, and changed to a condition known as secondary dentine, which provides almost as hard a surface as that of the original enamel. By this process the animal will gradually wear its teeth flat, but these worn and flattened teeth are perfectly sound teeth. The teeth of ancient races and of modern primitive races show well this dentine reaction. Human teeth may be ground down by wear and tear, and react to the grinding influence. But in modern civilized Man the reaction is very much diminished, and in the majority of cases, when the enamel is worn through, the fate of the tooth is sealed, since the dentine, instead of reacting, becomes the site of decay.

We have seen that in the whole Primate (and the whole arboreal) stock there has been a recession of the jaw. In one way this feature has been carried to very definite human lengths by very definite human methods When

arrived at its highest Anthropoid stage, the still relatively
large tooth-bearing (alveolar) margin of the jaws is well
in advance of the rest of the jaws. The tooth-bearing
surfaces and the teeth project. The upper jaw is prognathous, and the lower jaw has a very receding chin.
With the abbreviation of the alveolar margin in Man, the
prognathism disappears and the chin makes its appearance. The gradations in this change are very beautifully
seen in the remains of ancient Man and also in the jaws
of existing primitive Man (see Fig. 32). The mandible

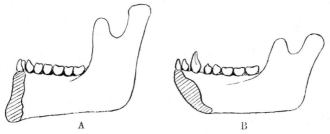

FIG. 32.—ONE HALF OF THE LOWER JAW OF (A) HOMO AND (B)
A MONKEY, TO SHOW THE PROMINENCE OF THE TOOTH-
BEARING MARGIN IN B AND OF THE CHIN IN A.

of the " Piltdown individual " is notorious, with its
advanced alveolar margin and receding chin. The
prognathous savage is proverbial. Man developed a chin
by the shrinkage of the alveolar margin of his jaw, consequent upon the diminishing demands made upon the
teeth, the functions of which were so largely usurped by
the hands. Modern and civilized Man seems to be in
some danger of losing even his chin as the whole mandible
becomes reduced. First, the recession of the tooth-
bearing margin makes the lower margin conspicuous,
and a chin is developed; and now the lower margin seems
to be disposed to follow in the train of the upper. The
dawn of a chinless aristocracy is no pleasing picture in
the later stages of human evolution; and yet the recession
of the modern jaw is not to be denied.

CHAPTER XVI

THE FACE AND THE CRANIUM

WE have followed some of the phases by which hand-feeding and alteration of life-habit have led to the recession of the snout region, and we have seen the influence which this recession exerts upon the dental series; but its influences are felt in many other ways, and some other of the accompanying phenomena must receive passing attention. The snout recedes as a part of a general evolution proceeding in arboreal life, and one other feature (to be dealt with later) which accompanies it is the steadily increasing growth of the brain. The skull as a whole may be said to consist of two parts—a part which is a containing bony case for the brain and the sense organs, and a part which is the skeleton of the mechanism for obtaining and masticating food (see Fig. 33).

In the lowest arboreal animals, the second or facial part is preponderately large in proportion to the first or cranial part, but the relations of the two parts are soon altered in arboreal evolution. The growing brain demands a large brain case; the diminishing jaws require less bony basis. In this way the configuration of the skull is profoundly altered, for not only do the jaws shrink back, but the brain case protrudes. Apart altogether from the mere evidence of the relative sizes of the bony parts in a skeleton, there is seen in this evolution a gradual change in the arteries and veins associated with these two constituents of the head region. The internal carotid artery enters the cranium to supply the brain, the external carotid artery runs to the face and supplies the whole facial area with blood; the internal jugular vein returns the blood from the brain, and the external jugular vein drains the area supplied by the external carotid artery. These two sets of vessels are of varying importance in different animals. Primitively, the external carotids and the external jugulars are by far the largest and most important vessels in the head region, and the internal carotids and internal jugulars are, relatively, inconsiderable channels. But in arboreal life, with hand-feeding and increasing brain growth, their

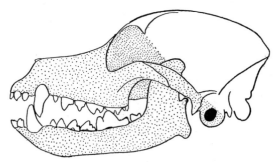

FIG. 33.—OUTLINE OF THE SKULL OF A DOG, TO SHOW THE RELATIVE PORTIONS DEVOTED TO THE SKELETON OF THE FACE AND TO THE SKELETON OF THE BRAIN CAVITY.

relative importance becomes altered, and finally in Man and in the higher Primates the internal carotids and internal jugulars far outweigh in size and importance the arteries and veins of the facial area. The gross changes which take place in the contour of the head have already been touched on, and they need no further emphasis, since they are conspicuous. A primitive arboreal Insectivore, such as *Tupaia*, has a relatively small head and a long snouty face (see Fig. 37); many Lemurs have snout regions almost as long, but others, such as *Tarsius spectrum*, have faces which are already distinctly flat (see Fig. 70). In Monkeys and Anthropoids, although the jaws protrude considerably in the adults of some species, the rounded skull case and flattened forehead dominate

7

the snout region as features of the head and face (see
Fig. 34). It is noteworthy that when for any reason
elongation of the nose becomes characteristic of any
species of monkey, this elongation is produced quite
apart from any reversion to a condition of prolonged
snout region. In the Proboscis Monkey (*Nasalis larvatus*) the nose reaches a remarkable degree of prominence,
but there is no involvement of the maxilla or mandible
in this new departure, and the same tendency is shown,

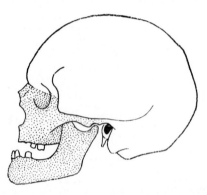

FIG. 34.—OUTLINE OF A HUMAN SKULL, TO SHOW THE RELATIVE
PORTIONS DEVOTED TO THE SKELETON OF THE FACE AND TO
THE SKELETON OF THE BRAIN CAVITY.

but to a lesser degree, in the curious Snub-Nosed Monkey
(*Rhinopithecus roxellanæ*).

These general alterations of the configuration of the
head and face lead to several changes, especially in the
position of the sense organs, which are probably of the
greatest importance. When an animal has a fully elongated snout region, it may be said to possess a long face
with an eye situated upon each side of it; but when the
snout region has undergone complete recession, it may
be said to have a flat face with two eyes situated upon
the front of it. The mere fact of the recession of the
snout produces this change, for the two eyes are turned

to the front as the elongated muzzle shrinks between them.

As the eyes begin to take up a forward position, a bar of bone forms behind them and intervenes between them and the space at the side of the skull in which the muscles of the jaw lie. In the Tree Shrews, the orbit has already commenced its separation from the temporal fossa; in *Tarsius spectrum,* the separation is complete, as we might imagine from the shortness of its face, but in all the other Lemurs the orbit and the temporal fossa communicate freely. In all the Monkeys and Anthropoid Apes, as in Man, the orbital cavity is an entirely separated compartment surrounded by bony walls and containing the eyeball and its associated muscles, nerves, and vessels. The bringing of the eyes to the front of the face and their lodgement in separated bony orbital cavities has, in all probability, far-reaching effects; but it must be looked upon only as a part of the general process of change in head formation brought about by hand-feeding in arboreal life. Another factor not to be disregarded is the change to which we will allude more fully later—the alteration of the head poise. Some consideration of this change is inseparable from a study of the recession of the snout region. When the face becomes so short that the whole skull is balanced upon its condyles, a complete change takes place in the axis of the principal movements of the head upon the trunk, and a greatly increased range is given to these movements. The arboreal Primates may nod their heads backwards and forwards, as in the human method of saying " Yes." This movement takes place between the condyles of the skull and the first cervical vertebra, and it is the primitive movement of raising and lowering the head common to all Mammals. But they also have an enormously increased power of turning the head from side to side, in the human method of signifying " No." This movement takes place between the first and second, as well as, to a lesser extent, between the other cervical vertebræ; but a wide range of movement is permitted in the neighbourhood of the skull before the other joints of the neck are involved.

This ability to turn the head quickly in any direction has had its influence upon the principal sense organs. Both eyes may be directed immediately, and at the same time, towards an object which attracts attention. In *Tarsius*, which possesses a wonderfully mobile head poise, there seems almost a tendency for the head movements to replace the movements of the enormous eyes, but in all other Primates, the head mobility merely supplements and aids the mobility of the eyeballs.

The head may be tilted into any conceivable position, so as to be placed at the greatest advantage to catch a sound proceeding from any direction. The sense organs may be brought into greater harmony and their teachings may be correlated by this mobility of the head, and, indeed, it is this mobility which has replaced that seen in lower animals in the pinna itself. An arboreal animal which has arrived at this stage does not " cock " or " prick " its ears when it hears a sound, but turns its mobile head so that it can catch the sound to greatest advantage, and at the same time bring the cause of the sound under the observation of its eyes.

Man and the Anthropoids have lost all trace of the useful movements of the external ear upon the scalp, but he and the arboreal Primates have compensated for this in the increased power to move the head—a power permitted by the altered configuration of the skull consequent upon the recession of the snout region.

CHAPTER XVII

THE SPINOUS PROCESSES OF THE VERTEBRAL COLUMN

In all works which deal with Comparative Anatomy, or with Anthropology, much attention is devoted to the human distinctions of poise of body. Various architectural features of the human body are modelled upon a plan somewhat different from that seen in most other animals, and these alterations of structural details are, for the most part, associated with a typical human poise of body. All these points have been eagerly seized upon as definite and measurable human features, and without turning aside now for any discussion of theories concerning them, it is our business to see if any of these features were impressed upon the body of Man as a result of his philogenetic youth spent among the branches. Most of the problems concern, in some measure, the vertebral column as the central axis around which the rest of the body is disposed. There are, for example, the questions of the poise of the head upon the neck, the presence of the sinuous curves of the vertebral column —cervical, dorsal, lumbar, and sacral curvatures; the actual method by which vertebra articulates with vertebra; the varying size, shape, and number of the elements which compose different regions of the column; and finally the manner in which the column articulates with the pelvic girdle.

We will start our examination of the backbone in a somewhat irregular way by considering, not the general curves and articulations of the whole column, but the characters of those processes which project, one from the dorsal aspect of each vertebra, and which are named *spinous processes* or *neural spines*. These spinous processes stand up in line all down the middle of the back, and to them are attached portions of the great muscle (M. erector spinæ) which acts upon the vertebral column. In actual disposition these spinous processes differ greatly in different animals; and the most conspicuous differences are to be noted in the direction in which they slope. Some, or all of them, may stand up quite straight, or they may lean towards the head end, or the tail end, of the animal. In the Reptiles, the arrangement of the spines is comparatively simple, for in most existing types all the processes stand directly upwards, or they are directed slightly backwards at their free tips. There is a very primitive plan, seen in many Reptiles, both living and extinct, as well as in some existing and many extinct Mammals, in which the vertebra to which the pelvic girdle is united forms a definite landmark by possessing an upright spinous process. All the vertebræ in front of this one may have their spines directed slightly backwards towards it, or with some variation displayed in the forward spines, uprightness is again found in the spine of this pelvic or sacral vertebra.

In many extinct reptilian forms the only truly upright spine is at the pelvis. In the *Gavial* some ten anterior spines point backwards, about nine are upright, and five are directed slightly forwards. In the modern Nilotic Crocodile some seventeen anterior spines are directed backwards, the last rib-bearing vertebra having an erect spine, and being followed by some five elements in which the spines are directed slightly forwards; and after that comes the pelvic region with an upright spine again.

The upright spine of the pelvic vertebra of the Reptiles entitles this vertebra especially to the distinctive name of *anticlinal vertebra*. This may be the only spine in the whole vertebral column which does not slope, but we have already seen that in the Crocodile (and in some other existing Reptiles) another upright spine is beginning to be evident at the hind end of the rib series, and this is the one to which the term *anticlinal vertebra* is usually applied in mammalian anatomy.

Within the limits of the Mammalia, the condition of the trend of the spinous processes varies enormously. Among the Prototheria, *Echidna* and *Proechidna* show a series of cervical, dorsal, and lumbar spines which point uniformly backwards towards the sacral region (see Fig. 35). This is apparently the primitive mammalian

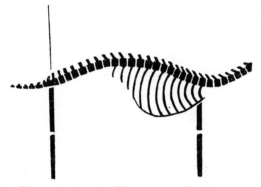

Fig. 35.—Diagram of the Vertebral Column of an Animal in which All the Spinous Processes are Retroverted.

as well as the primitive reptilian condition, and, as such, is seen in an extraordinarily varied collection of extinct species embracing such forms as *Toxodon*, *Arsinotherium*, *Mylodon*, etc. In *Ornithordhynchus*, there is a change, for though all the cervical and dorsal spines slope acutely backwards, those of the three lumbar vertebræ slope forwards, there being an anticlinal element at the hind end of the rib-bearing series. In the Metatheria and Eutheria, the very widest divergence in spinal inclination is seen, and it seems most probable that some functional demand determines the variations met with. Owen paid attention to this point, and recognized clearly the

underlying cause of the variations. Some fifty years ago
Paul Topinard dealt partially with this problem, which
had previously engaged the attention of Paul Broca.
But these two authors considered little more than the
end of the story, for they took most note of those changes
which have taken place in so short a chapter as that
comprised in the study of the higher Primates and Man.
It is, however, necessary to embrace far more than this
in the study of what Topinard termed " anteversion and
ʳʳ̓troversion " of the spinous processes. If we take the
skeleton of such a well-known animal as the dog it is at
once apparent that the spines of the cervical and most
of the dorsal vertebræ are " retroverted," that the
penultimate dorsal vertebra is " anticlinal," and the two
last dorsal and all the lumbar vertebræ have spines that
are " anteverted," another upright spinous process ap-
pearing on the sacrum. The anticlinal vertebra which
is situated, in the dog, near the end of the dorsal, or rib-
bearing, series has also been termed the region of the
" centre of motion "; and it is easy to realize, in watching
a greyhound looping along, that this is a perfectly well
justified term. The anticlinal vertebra indicates that
the animal possessing it has the power of bending its
vertebral column as a spring is bent, and that the apex
of the bend is situated at this particular point. The
presence of such a vertebra in the backbone, whether
of a recent animal or a fossil, shows clearly that the
animal could flex and extend its vertebral column about
this central point, and that its spine could be bent, and
could be straightened out again as a spring in the ordinary
activities of the animal (see Fig. 36). These things are
clear enough when we look at the skeleton of a dog, or a
hare, and weave into the bones the picture of the animal
laying itself out, and doubling itself up, as it goes at full
speed. But there is, as we have seen, another condition
—that seen in some primitive Reptiles and Mammals—
in which the anticlinal vertebra is situated, not in the

middle of the back, but at the point where the legs and
pelvis hinge upon the spine, at the junction of tail and
body.   In these animals the mechanism of spinal movements is obviously of a different nature, and a whole
series of correlated anatomical details makes it clear that
no spring-like bending of the backbone takes place at or

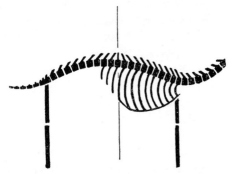

Fig. 36.—Diagram of the Vertebral Column of an Animal
   in which the Spinous Processes are Anteverted and
   Retroverted to a Definite Centre of Movement.

near its mid-point.   But the pelvic anticlinal vertebra
is a true centre of movement in animals built upon this
type.   Towards the fixed pelvic girdle the head and neck
and the whole of the trunk may be pulled, and raised, as
the arm of a crane; towards the same fixed point the
usually elongated tail may be similarly pulled up.   This
is a simple and primitive anatomical plan, and it is
adapted to simple and primitive types of movement.
The range of body movements possible with this plan of
arrangement of spinous processes and their associated
muscles would appear to comprise such actions as crawl-
ing, waddling, shuffling, that type of running best termed
ambling, and simple aquatic paddling.
    In all these actions there is no regional bending of the
vertebral column, no centre of movement save that
situated at the point above the hips.   This is the mechanism, and these are the movements of most of the existing

limbed Reptiles; the same type of movement, we may fairly hazard, was characteristic of the extinct gigantic forms of which the bony evidences of the mechanism are so clearly preserved.

Among the plastic Mammals, the evidence of function is very easily seen. Animals which hop, jump, spring, leap, or gallop show the presence of well-marked anteversion and retroversion of the spinous processes. Nearly all Rodents and Insectivores possess this feature. Of the Carnivora, the cats which spring, and the dogs which leap and gallop, have a strongly divided series of spinous processes, while the shuffling bears show a vertebral column of which all the spines anterior to the sacrum are directed backwards. Leaping and galloping Ungulates, which can use both fore-limbs and both hind-limbs alternately in their full stride, provide the classical example of the anticlinal spinous process at the penultimate rib-bearing vertebra. Some very striking exceptions are worth noticing among the Ungulates. We have already called attention to the curious gait of the Giraffe, which in quiet progression advances both limbs of the same side at the same time. It is interesting to find that in this animal all the cervical, dorsal, and lumbar spinous processes slope backwards—there is no centre of movement until the region of the hips is reached. I should imagine that, even when hard pressed, a Giraffe cannot break into a gallop, and that it possesses little or no power of jumping, but I know of no authoritative observations upon these points. The spinous processes of Okapia are arranged upon the same simple plan, and I presume that it possesses the same peculiar gait, and the same probable limitations of activity as the Giraffe. It is not surprising that the lumbering Elephant, with its peculiarly rigid backbone, should have no dorsal centre of movement, and no anticlinal vertebra, and the same feature is shared by such simple paddlers as the Sirenia.

It would take us too far aside from our present purpose to discuss the question, but we may note the observation that, judging by such skeletal remains as have been preserved, the Mammals, at an early period of their history, were represented by an extraordinary number of forms the gait of which we may presume to have been but little better than a simple reptilian shuffle. The active galloping and springing animals are their changed and modern representatives.

In the case of arboreal animals the problem is apparently complicated at the outset by the fact that, while some perfected tree-climbers show a highly specialized series of anteverted and retroverted spines, separated by a well-marked anticlinal vertebra, others, none the less well fitted for a thoroughly arboreal life, have a series of uniformly directed spines, all being retroverted (even if only slightly so) towards the pelvis.

It is easy to furnish a satisfactory explanation for these differences by appealing to the varied, and perfectly distinctive, methods of tree-climbing adopted by different arboreal animals, but it is by no means easy to determine what may be the relation of these two forms to each other. Either type (the divided, or the uniform spinous series) might be primitive in the tree-climbers, and the one might subsequently be derived from the other by alteration of function as displayed in climbing methods. Again, both types may have been definite legacies in arboreal animals derived from differently constructed primitive stocks; both may have been inherited types with which the animals took to an arboreal life, and on which they have moulded their arboreal activities. Or, both of these alternative factors may be in action, when we regard the whole wide range of arboreal Mammals. It seems not unlikely that this last supposition is true.

Taking a group of animals so perfectly arboreal as the Edentate Sloths of South America (*Bradypodidæ*), we see, combined with a very peculiar fashion of arboreal

activity, a vertebral column possessing a uniformly
sloping series of spinous processes. The question that
presents itself is, Does this spinal arrangement represent
the inherited handicap of these arboreal animals, an
ancestral birthright which has determined and limited
their peculiar climbing habits; or have their individualities
as tree-clingers modified a spinal column which may at
one time have possessed the doubly sloping series of
spines indicative of greater activity ? The present-day
arboreal Sloths possess a backbone of the lumbering-
terrestrial walkers. Are they derived from a lumbering-
walking stock of which some of the smaller, lighter
members have taken to the trees and become lumbering
tree-clingers, since that was the limit of their arboreal
possibilities ? The evidence of paleontology certainly
points towards the last conclusion as being nearer the
truth.

The extinct relations of the Sloths are well known.
On the strength of the evidence afforded by *Megatherium*,
Mylodon, and other well-studied gigantic fossil Edentates,
it seems justifiable to regard the modern Sloths as diminu-
tive descendants of lumbering animals, and to look upon
their restricted arboreal activities as the necessary result
of their ancestry. We may assume the correctness of
Owen's conclusion that *Mylodon robustus* reared itself
against the trees in tripod fashion, and pulling down
the branches, browsed upon their leaves.

From such a beginning we would picture some smaller
members of the same stock going farther than this, and
clinging to the branches in their search for food; and in
this manner we would picture the Sloths becoming
arboreal.

Even when they had reached the tree-tops, and had
definitely made their homes among them, they were still
imited by the handicap which their ancestral terrestrial
shuffling gait had imposed upon them; and though no
animals are more thoroughly arboreal than the existing

Sloths, it cannot be said that their arboreal activities, although distinctive enough, tend to lead far in the struggle of evolution.

If this be the true history of the arboreal *Bradypodidæ*, it would seem to be one not easily applied to the origin of the arboreal Primate stock. No lumbering gait, or mere clinging to branches, seems to have led them to the tree-tops; and, indeed, as we have seen in a previous section, an early acquired mammalian activity appears the most probable factor in bringing about the enterprise. Taken as a whole, the Primates show a distinctly retro-verted and anteverted series of dorso-lumbar spinous processes, the two sets being separated by an anticlinal vertebra marking a centre of movement, which is very obvious in the arboreal activities of most monkeys.

The same conditions are present in most members of the Insectivora. Among the *Menotyphlidæ*, the Oriental Tree Shrews (*Tupaiadæ*), which are deserving of especial notice, have twelve ribs, the spines of the vertebræ anterior to the tenth dorsal slope backwards, the tenth or eleventh is upright, and the nine posterior spines slope forwards. These are active arboreal creatures jumping from branch to branch, and having a very definite centre of movement at the hind end of the thoracic region (see Fig. 37).

There are many reasons for supposing that, in some such form as a primitive tree-haunting Insectivore, a picture of an earlier stage of the Primate phylum is to be seen most perfectly among living Mammals. Some exceedingly primitive form, of which a very much elabo-rated modern evolution may be seen in the existing *Tupaiadæ*, probably pioneered the Primate stock in the conquest of the branches; this pioneer form was, in all probability, a small active animal, perhaps with the commencing possession of a centre of movement situated at the hinder end of the thoracic vertebræ.

Great interest centres round the Lemurs in the study

Fig. 37. – A Typical Tree Shrew. Adult Female of *Tupaia
ferruginea.*
From a spirit specimen.

of the disposition of the spinous processes. In this feature the majority of them follow the Tree Shrews, and those that are characterized by special activity present a remarkably double-sloped series of spines. Some Lemurs might almost be called arboreal jumpers, and among them the Bornean *Tarsius* and the African *Galagos* are most prominent; in these animals the forward slope of the lumbar spines is particularly acute. But with some other Lemurs the most puzzling feature of the problem is introduced, for *Nycticebus*, as a type of the Asiatic Slow Lemurs, presents a series of spines as uniformly retroverted as that seen in the Sloths themselves. Some confusion between the Sloths and Slow Lemurs has, in bygone days, been a stumbling-block in systematic zoology. Is this similiarity of the backbone another feature which might cause the animals to be confounded, and is it one that might point to any real philogenetic affinity in the stocks of the Slow Lemurs and the Sloths ? In this feature we have seen some reason for believing that Sloths were derived from a lumbering terrestrial stock, and it may fairly be asked if the same reasoning should not apply to the case of *Nycticebus*. We have pictured the stock of the Lemurs as arising most probably from a small active animal; are we to regard the Slow Lemurs as having a different origin ?

Probably the correct answer is that the Slow Lemurs show so many points of affinity with the rest of the Lemurs that they can only be regarded as altered members of the same stock. " Although they vary considerably in structure from the more typical Lemurs, there can be no doubt that the Slow Lemurs possess a true Lemurine structure in many important particulars, so that they must have had a common origin with the true Lemurs " (Sclater). We are bound, therefore, by our present limitations of knowledge to regard this as a case of convergence. We have previously noted the peculiarities of the arboreal habits of *Nycticebus*. It is a tree-clinger more nearly than a true tree-climber, and moreover it shows a definite tendency to carry out its arboreal activities in an inverted position. It is therefore to be presumed that the adoption of this habit has led to a modification of its erector spinæ muscle and its spinous processes, and that by its slothful habits *Nycticebus* has, in this respect, arrived at the state to which the Edentate Sloths were bound by their inherited disabilities.

The case of the Slow Lemurs is all the more interesting since the absence of a dorso-lumbar centre of movement, and the presence of a practically uniform series of spines, are seen in another group of arboreal Primates. *Nycticebus* does not leap from branch to branch, it takes no spring from its hind-limbs, it does not jump to its next arboreal station, but reaches out for it and grasps it, and upon the ground it crawls and shuffles along. Now, much the same conditions are seen in the Anthropoids. The Giant Apes, though active enough and expert climbers, do not spring from their hind-limbs, or leap about the branches as the smaller monkeys do. Wallace has described the Orang-utan in its natural state as " moving slowly along, hanging from the branches by its arms," and as " moving along a large limb of a tree in a semi-erect posture." Both these modes of progression are typical of the Anthropoids; the first, according to Wallace, is unusual in *Simia satyrus*, but it is the one which is characteristic of the smaller agile Anthropoids known as the Gibbons (*Hylobates*).

The Chimpanzee adopts the same methods of climbing, methods which involve a semi-erect foot balance combined with a dependence upon a powerful hand grasp. More rapid translation from branch to branch, or from tree to tree, is not performed by a spring from the resting feet, but by a swing from the grasping hands. A group of monkeys passing from tree to tree in the jungle will jump those gaps where branches fail to meet, but a party of Gibbons will swing themselves across the gap, releasing one hand-grasp only to gain another. It is in this fashion that human performers on the high trapeze pass from one swinging bar to another.

It is this factor, a purely arboreal one, that has led to the typical condition of the anthropoid vertebral column, and determined the disposition of its muscles and the arrangement of its bony prominences. The springing point in the middle of the backbone is absent, and the column acts as a whole; its spines are in uniform series, and its accompanying muscles support it as a pillar, rather than bend it as a spring.

There is nothing in this that is peculiar to Man, nothing that has any relation to the attainment of any distinctive human attribute; it was among the branches, as an outcome of the arboreal life, that the uniformly sloping series of spinous processes, seen in the human vertebral column, was attained.

Among the Anthropoids themselves some minor variations are seen in the disposition of the spinous processes. In the Gibbons the series is quite uniform, but in the large Anthropoids the spines in the cervical region are peculiarly elongated. More than this, in the Gorilla the spine of the third cervical vertebra is strongly anteverted, and at times the fourth and fifth share in a slight forward slope. Again, at the hind end of the series some variability is seen, for some of the posterior spines are not distinctly retroverted. In Man this variability in the posterior spines is also present, for the lumbar spinous processes do not always slope in quite the same manner. In some primitive human races there is even a tendency to anteversion in the posterior spines, which shows itself at times quite distinctly in the first sacral vertebra

8

CHAPTER XVIII

THE POISE OF THE HEAD AND THE CURVES OF THE SPINE

THE differences seen in the disposition of the cervical spinous processes in the Anthropoids and in Man are due to, and involve, yet another factor which may be termed the poise of the head upon the vertebral column.

This subject has been so fully investigated by comparative anatomists that little need be said here concerning it.

The skull is hinged to the foremost vertebra by its two condyles, and between these occipital condyles and the articulating surfaces of the first vertebra the human movement of nodding the head to and fro takes place. The position of the two condyles relatively to other anatomical features of the skull varies enormously in animals adopting different life postures. The condyles may be situated right at the hinder end of the skull, they may be just beneath the hind end, or they may be situated some distance forward along its base. In pronograde quadrupedal animals, such as the dog, the head is jointed to the vertebral column by condyles situated at the extreme hind end of the skull; the nose is directed forwards in line with the vertebral column, and the skull is braced in position by a strong ligament—the ligamentum nuchæ—and by muscles passing from the vertebræ to the back of the cranium (see Fig. 38). In animals which are not purely pronograde quadrupeds, an alteration takes place; the poise of the head becomes changed and the site of the condyles shifts upon the skull. In arboreal animals this change becomes very evident,

114

for with the body held even partially, and only occasionally upright, the eyes and face still need to be directed forwards, and an angle is introduced between the long

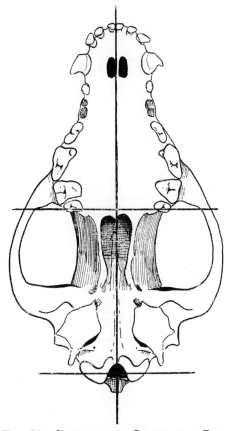

FIG. 38.—BASE OF THE SKULL OF A DOG.

This and the following three figures are drawn with the dioptograph from skulls which are orientated strictly in the same plane.   The relative positions of the condyles are therefore directly comparable in the series of drawings.

axis of the skull and face, and the long axis of the vertebral column.   This angle can be produced, as occasion demands, in the articulations of an ordinary quadruped.

In the normal method of progression a dog carries its head nearly in line with its vertebral column, but when it sits up to beg it bends its head and neck so that its eyes and face are still directed forwards, and the head becomes almost at right angles to the axis of its vertebral column. This position becomes habitual in the arboreal

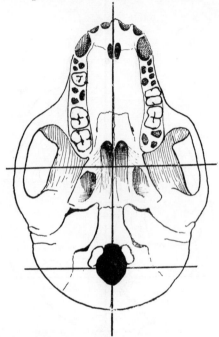

FIG. 39.—BASE OF THE SKULL OF A BABOON (*Cynocephalus*).

Primates, for in them the trunk has so frequently to be more or less upright, and in proportion to the permanency of this position there comes about a shifting of the site of the condyles.

Posture alone determines this change, for the more quadrupedal Baboons (*Cynocephalus*) do not share so fully in this feature, which is so characteristic of their truly arboreal allies (see Fig. 39). In most monkeys the occipital condyles are situated well forward upon the base of the skull, and in the Anthropoids they are still further forward. In Man the head is practically balanced upon the first cervical vertebra (see Figs. 40 and 41).

The general factor which underlies this forward migration of the condyles is involved early in arboreal life, and it is one that proceeds far in animals that are still purely

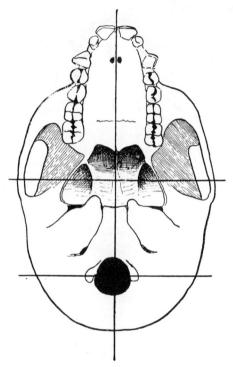

FIG. 40.—BASE OF THE SKULL OF A MONKEY (*Cercopithecus*).

arboreal. The final changes which have taken place in Man might be ranked among the finishing touches of human development, for they consist, not so much in any further forward migration of the site of the condyles, as in the culmination of that other process which we have termed the recession of the snout region. In the giant Anthropoids the head itself has already attained

all the essentials of the human poise, but the preponderately large face and jaws, in the adult Gorilla especially,
demand for their proper balance a large muscular leverage
applied to the back of the head. It is this muscle mass
which gives these animals their apparently short bull-

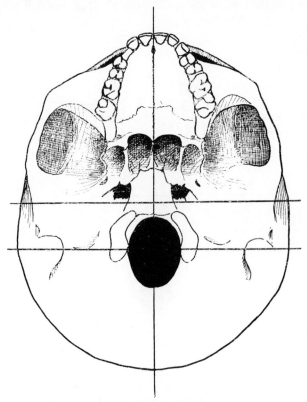

FIG. 41.—BASE OF THE HUMAN SKULL.

necks, and which, acting from the spinous processes of
the cervical vertebræ, elongates these processes and pulls
them towards the skull.

The poise of the skull, and the forward migration of the
occipital condyles and foramen magnum, are arboreal
features. Finishing touches have been put upon the

human condition by the final phases of the recession of the snout region.

With the question of the curves of the vertebral column we need deal but briefly, for the subject is one which finds ample discussion in every work upon anthropology. In pronograde quadrupeds the backbone rises as one long, low-pitched arch from the point where it is supported by the fore-limb, to a maximum in the dorso-lumbar region, and then falls again to the point where it is supported by the hind-limbs. The weight of the trunk is carried from an arch which is supported upon pillars (limbs) at its two extremities. It is this arch which in some animals has a springing point at its centre. In front of the anterior supporting pillar the spine bends up again for the carriage of the head. This time the arch is reversed, for while the curve of the back is convex upon its dorsal side, the curve of the neck is convex ventrally. Again, behind the posterior supporting pillar the spine is also bent upwards; here, at the sacro-vertebral angle, the bending dorsalwards is more acute; but from this point, the curve is slightly downwards once more, the posterior or sacral arch being like the dorsal arch in miniature, but generally still more flattened (see Figs. 35 and 36).

In arboreal animals these curves are also well marked, and the changes which they undergo are quite definite. Arboreal uprightness, in the sense of the assumption of a sitting posture, has a well-marked influence upon the primitive curves. Some monkeys, as they sit up, spend the greater part of their time with the trunk supported vertical upon their ischial prominences, and in these animals the dorso-lumbar curve tends to be, not one long pitch as in the quadrupeds, but an arch subdivided into an anterior sharper curve over the thoracic part of the body, and a more gradual curve over the abdominal part. The dorso-lumbar curve tends to be concentrated as a dorsal curve, while the lumbar region is scarcely

arched at all. This is, of course, merely an adaptation
to posture, and as such it is seen in other, and non-
arboreal, animals which tend to carry the trunk axis
vertical, no matter what may be the relation of the hind-
limb to the trunk. A flattened lumbar region is present
in the Kangaroos (*Macropus*), and it is the same in the
Jerboas (*Dipus*), which hop with the trunk axis nearly
vertical. Arboreal life brought about a lumbar flattening
early, since trunk uprightness is an easily attained outcome of the climbing habit, but it also—in the Anthropoid
Apes—carried it a stage further than this.

A lumbar flattening suffices for an animal which holds
its trunk upright upon the basis of its flexed lower limbs,
and it suffices for animals which sit and hop upright.
It will not suffice, however, when the trunk uprightness
has to be combined with extended lower limbs. If an
animal is to maintain its trunk and its lower limbs in one
continuous axis, something more than a lumbar flattening
is required, and a reversed lumbar curve is introduced.
In most monkeys the reversed lumbar curve is already
present in some slight degree. In *Cercopithecus palatinus*
it is perfectly definite, and the same may be said for all
thoroughly arboreal monkeys, when the vertebral column
is examined in its natural state; but the curvature disappears altogether in the skeleton (see Fig. 42). The
reason for this is that the curvature is caused by the
shaping of the soft intervertebral discs, rather than by
any change in the bones themselves, and when these
discs are lost in the preparation of the skeleton, the
presence of the curves is ignored in the subsequent
mounting of the specimen. If our knowledge be derived
from the actual animals, rather than from museum
skeletons, we cannot deny that a lumbar curve convex
forwards is already present in the monkeys.

The straightening of the lower limb upon the trunk is
an extremely important factor in primate evolution, and
we will follow Professor Keith in regarding the habit of

hand suspension, seen in the Gibbons, as the agent which made it a definite possession of the Anthropoids.   As the Gibbon travels about among the branches, its trunk and

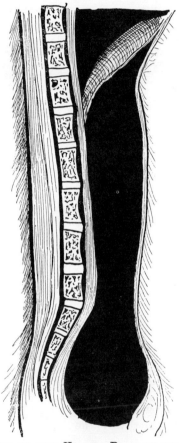

Fig. 42.—Section of the Hinder Part of the Body of a Monkey (*Cercopithecus palatinus*), to show the Incipient Forward Curve in the Lumbar Region of the Spine.

hind-limbs are dependent while it swings with its long arms from branch to branch. The body and leg axis is straightened almost as much as it is in upright walking Man. The Gibbons show a curvature in the lumbar region, the convexity of which is directed forwards and which is better marked than the same curve in any monkey. In the Gibbons the bones themselves have begun to share in the change, and the curvature is evident in the dried skeleton. This lumbar curve is present with

FIG. 43.—THE NORMAL CURVES OF A HUMAN VERTEBRAL COLUMN AS SEEN IN A SECTION THROUGH AN UPRIGHT BODY.

an ever-increasing perfection through the Giant Apes to the lower, and finally to the higher, races of mankind (see Fig. 43).

No doubt it is a feature which is called into being by the erectness of the trunk upon the lower limbs, but it must not be regarded as a feature stamped upon the human frame by terrestrial bipedal orthograde habits; it was begot among the branches, it led to greater possibilities, and only its finishing touches were put on by upright walking upon the surface of the earth.

CHAPTER XIX

THE PELVIS AND THE VISCERA

THE arboreal alteration of body poise makes itself felt in other skeletal and visceral features than those related solely to the backbone and the skull; for, at the other end of the vertebral column, the pelvis undergoes marked changes in arboreal life. The primitive pelvis, such as the earliest Mammals inherited, is a very definite structure articulated in a very definite manner, and in all essentials it is of the same type as that seen in the generalized Reptiles both living and extinct.

Such a primitive pelvis consists of two lateral halves, each half being composed of three elements: one a dorsal element, articulating with the vertebral column, and the other two, which are ventral elements, articulating with each other in the middle line of the ventral surface of the body. The dorsal element (*ilium*) articulates with the vertebral column at the sacrum, over a sacro-iliac joint surface which involves both the rib element (*pleurapophysis*) and the transverse process element (*diapophysis*), which enter into the formation of the sacrum. The two ventral elements articulate at an elongated symphysis, which involves both bones (*pubis* and *ischium*), and is therefore an ischio-pubic symphysis. These types of sacro-iliac and ischio-pubic joints are characteristic of quadrupedal animals that have four equally developed supporting limbs, and they are obviously dependent upon the mechanical demands for supporting the body upon the limbs in pronograde animals. With a change of body poise, an alteration in pelvic architecture, to meet

123

the new conditions, is evidenced in a wide series of vertebrate forms, and, with an exchange of pronograde quadrupedal progression for arboreal uprightness, the pelvis becomes greatly modified. In a simple mechanical way we may regard the sacrum of the pronograde as slung between the two ilia, slung from two separate points of suspension, the one on its costal portion (*pleura-pophysis*), and the other on its transverse process element

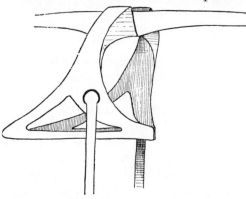

FIG. 44.—PURELY DIAGRAMMATIC REPRESENTATION OF THE PELVIS OF A THOROUGHLY QUADRUPEDAL MAMMAL.

Note the way in which the sacrum is articulated with the ilia at the sacro-iliac joint, and the meeting of the pubes and ischia at the ischio-pubic symphysis.

(*diapophysis*). The visceral weight is supported upon an elongated ventral symphysis, which constitutes only one element in the supporting developments of the structures in the mid-ventral line of the body. Such a pelvis tends to be narrow from side to side, but elongated in its dorsiventral axis. With the assumption (even to a partial extent) of arboreal uprightness of the body axis, the body weight tends to be disposed round the vertebral column as round a vertical pillar, rather than to be slung from it as from a horizontal pole; and now the sacrum tends to be wedged between the two iliac bones, as the keystone of an arch disposed in a cranio-caudal rather than in a dorsi-ventral direction. This change produces an effect upon the sacro-iliac joint that we may sum up by saying that an elongated dorsi-ventral contact area becomes unnecessary, and is gradually replaced by an elongated cranio-caudal contact area.

Although there are some exceptions and irregularities in the application of this principle to the pelves of existing Mammals, still the exceptions are capable of explanation and do not detract from the general rule that with a change from quadrupedal to bipedal progression more sacral vertebræ enter into the formation of the joint, but less of the dorsi-ventral area of each vertebra is engaged by the ilia.

A common type of sacro-iliac joint, in purely prono-grade quadrupedal Mammals, is that in which but one sacral element is articulated with the ilia; and this one element is sunk deep between the two ilia, so that the joint surface involves the whole of its dorsi-ventral area, engaging both pleurapophysis and diapophysis elements which are represented in this area. In most of the Lemurs one whole sacral element, and from a quarter to a half of the next caudal element, are engaged in the sacro-iliac joint. In many New-World Monkeys the condition is the same, and in both cases these elements are deeply sunk between the ilia, so that the diapophyses are articular. In the Baboons one whole element, and three-quarters of another, are engaged. In most Old-World Monkeys nearly the whole of two sacral elements enter into the articulation, and the same condition is present in the pelvis of the upright *Indris* among the Lemurs. In the Anthropoids from two and a half to three sacral elements are involved, but the condition is subject to a considerable degree of variation in different individuals. In the Gibbons (*Hylobates lar*) nearly the whole of three elements is articular, and the articulation involves both pleurapophysis and diapophysis of the sacral vertebræ. In the Orang-utan the articulation varies; it may involve no more than the best part of two sacral vertebræ, or nearly the whole of three may enter into the joint. But the diapophyses of only two of the sacral vertebræ are, as a rule, involved. In both the Gorilla and the Chimpanzee the joint surface occupies from two and a half to three sacral vertebræ, but involves the diapophysis of only two elements. In Man the greatest variation is sexual, and the female articulation, as a rule, comprises only two or two and a half sacral vertebræ, while that of the male embraces from two and a half to three. In any case, an articulation evolving a diapophyseal element is a somewhat uncommon human anomaly.

It would therefore seem that the sacrum is being received between the ilia in a greater proportion of its length, but is freeing itself from articulation in some portion of its depth by (if it may be expressed thus) liberating its dorsal surface from joint contact with the ilia.

Hand in hand with this alteration of the sacro-iliac joint a change is proceeding in the ventral symphysis. This change may best be summed up by saying that the symphysial area becomes shortened progressively in the transition from pronograde poise to arboreal orthograde habit. The symphysis, which is first of all an ischio-pubic union in the mid-line, becomes opened from its caudal aspect, and more and more of the ischia are freed from the ventral union. By gradual stages the whole length of the ischia becomes liberated from the symphysis, and the two bones are splayed aside from each other. Next, the pubes share in the process, and from the condition of a true pubic symphysis, in which the whole of the ventral ends of the pubic bones are involved, there is developed the pubic symphysis typical of Man, in which only about a half of the ventral ends of the pubes enter into the articulation.

That this is an outcome of the modified method of

supporting the body weight is not to be doubted, despite some apparent contradictions, and it is to be remarked that in animals in which the body weight is not borne at all upon the hind-limbs (as in the Bats, etc.) no portion of the pelvic girdle meets in the mid-ventral line, and consequently no symphysis is developed.

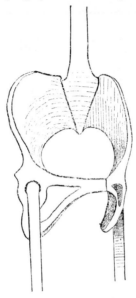

Fig. 45.—Purely Diagrammatic Representation of the Pelvis of an Orthograde Mammal.

Note the way in which the sacrum articulates with the ilia at the sacro-iliac joint, and the meeting of only a small area of the pubes at the pubic symphysis.

The pelvis has now, in its altered relation to the hind-limb, an entirely different mechanical design. There is a main weight-supporting arch behind, composed of the ilia, with the sacrum as the keystone of this arch. A subsidiary weight-supporting arch is developed in front, and this is represented by the subpubic arch. The old ventro-dorsal weight-supporting arch is superseded, and now the cavity of the pelvis need no longer be moulded

in an elongated form from back to front; it rather becomes
rounded, or even broadened from side to side. These
changes in the bony architecture of the pelvic girdle lead
naturally to changes in the disposition of the viscera
most intimately related to the pelvis. In particular the
splaying open of the hinder end of the symphysis produces

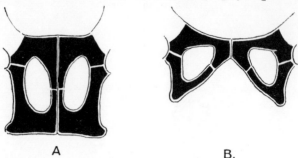

A   B.

Fig. 46.—Diagrammatic Representations of (A) Primitive
Mammalian and (B) Human Type of Ventral Symphysis.

marked alterations in the visceral outlets, since the
perineum shares in the changes. The form of the external genitalia in both sexes becomes modified by this
opening movement of the symphysis; and the external
reproductive orifices become situated beneath the pubic
arch, instead of occupying the hind end of an elongated
pelvic tunnel. The internal organs also become profoundly modified, and those channels which connect the
hollow viscera with the surface of the body become
abbreviated with the outfolding of the hind end of the
symphysis. Other visceral changes come about hand in
hand with this pelvic adaptation, and this for the reason
that both are the results of the altered poise in arboreal
activities. As the body axis becomes increasingly
upright, the disposition of the viscera within the body
cavities undergoes a purely mechanical alteration. It
may be said that the method of packing the organs in
the cavities is changed, simply for convenience, as the

axis of the cavities becomes modified. Since most of
the organs are suspended from the walls of the cavities
it is this method of suspension which naturally becomes

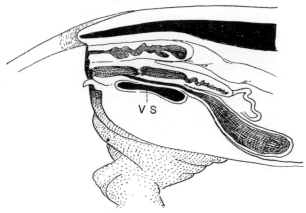

FIG. 47.—MEDIAN SECTION OF A YOUNG FEMALE PIG, TO SHOW
THE RELATION OF THE VENTRAL SYMPHYSIS (V.S.) TO THE
VISCERA.

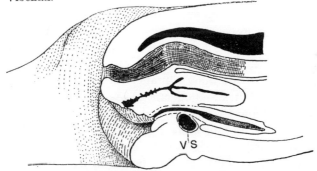

FIG. 48.—MEDIAN SECTION OF A FULL-TERM HUMAN FEMALE
FŒTUS, TO SHOW THE RELATION OF THE VENTRAL SYM-
PHYSIS (V.S.) TO THE VISCERA.

most markedly affected. Briefly, we may say that when
the trunk axis becomes more upright, all the viscera tend
to sink towards the hind end of the body, and they tend
to be suspended from the head end of the cavities rather
than from the dorsal aspect. There is no need to describe

9

these changes in any detail, since almost every individual
manifestation of them that is especially well marked in
Man has been seized upon as an example of the alterations
due to his orthograde bipedal habits, and, as a consequence, the subject has received sufficient attention in
the literature of physical anthropology. The heart
comes to be suspended from the cephalic end of the
thorax, rather than from its dorsal side, and so it rests
upon the upper surface of the diaphragm, rather than
upon the anterior wall of the chest. Changes in the
disposition of the lungs follow harmoniously this readjustment of the position of the heart.

In the abdominal cavity the same general effects are
seen. The viscera sink backwards. The liver is suspended more strongly from the lower surface of the
diaphragm, and the intestines obtain attachments which
sling them from the upper part of the cavity, as well as
from its dorsal wall. All these things are adjustments
to trunk uprightness—that trunk uprightness which is
early brought about in arboreal life—and, as such, they
make their appearance long before the stage at which
Man walked upright upon his two feet; for it must never
be forgotten that the trunk of an animal which climbs
up a tree, or sits upon a branch, is just as upright as is
that of a Man standing erect. As far as concerns the
abdominal and thoracic viscera, a man is as upright when
he sits as when he stands, and an arboreal animal which
sits and climbs among the branches is in a like case.

The upright poise of Man has been lauded as one of
his greatest distinctions. This praise of human uprightness has, without doubt, been carried to absurd extremes,
so also has the tendency to ascribe to this same uprightness
a multitude of human weaknesses and disabilities. This
visceral uprightness is no new thing, the readjustment
has been gradual, and some measure of it has been very
long established. It is easy to overdo the praise of the
poise. It is equally easy to overdo the condemnation of
it as a cause of many human ills.

CHAPTER XX

THE RESPIRATORY SYSTEM

WE will not deal directly with that portion of the respiratory system which is concerned with the production of voice, since the factors underlying the changes produced in these structures are not those that bring about the modifications in the disposition of the organs purely concerned in breathing.

Here we will only consider the effects produced upon the chest and lungs, and the method by which air is taken into the lungs. The alterations in the general shape of the chest, which have differentiated the human form from that seen in purely quadrupedal animals, are very well known, and are discussed in all works dealing with human morphology.*

These alterations are, as a rule, ascribed to the upright posture—and rightly; but, again, we must remember that the upright posture need not mean the erect walking posture, but may imply nothing more than mere arboreal uprightness. In brief, we may say that a typical quadrupedal animal, such as a dog, is narrow-chested. Its breastbone marks the keel of a chest, deep from breastbone to backbone, but narrow from side to side. An upright animal, on the other hand, tends to have a broad chest, the breastbone no longer protrudes as a keel, and the chest is shallow from breastbone to backbone, and broad from side to side. Man shows the extreme of this flattening of the chest; but the rounding of the quadrupedal chest is well seen in arboreal types quite low down in the mammalian scale. Indeed, although we speak of a phylogenetic flattening of the chest, we must also be prepared to admit that the narrow quadrupedal type of chest is itself a modification from the presumably flatter chest that was the possession of the first mammalian forms.

The change from the narrow pointed chest to the broad flat chest is, for the most part, effected by the falling backwards, towards the backbone, of the whole chest, as the animal becomes more adapted to maintaining its body axis upright. The ribs of a quadrupedal animal tend to dispose themselves as oval hoops, hung in their long axis from the backbone; the ribs of an animal with an upright axis tend to dispose themselves as rounded hoops, surrounding the backbone as hoops surround a pole.

In this way the backbone tends to become, not the ridge from which the hoops are hung, but a central prop within the circle of the hoops; to do this the backbone has to sink into the back of the series of hoops, pushing them in before it as it goes. This simple mechanical alteration effects a double change. In the quadrupedal animal the breastbone projects as a keel; the backbone projects as a ridge. In the animal with the upright axis the breastbone is merely part of the evenly rounded front of the chest, the backbone merely a part of the evenly rounded back. In Man the process culminates in a chest which is flat in front, and a back which is flat behind. This is a simple mechanical process; in no sense can it be said to be due to the assumption of the upright posture, if by that posture the erect walking posture is meant. It did not come suddenly into the possession of the human stock when that stock took to walking with the soles of the feet planted flat upon the level surface of the earth; it was already in being when, in life among the branches, the animal squatted or hung with its body erect. This is a change of bodily conformation, and, as such, needs treatment elsewhere; it does not so directly concern the function of respiration. This function has, however, been modified very distinctly by the habit of tree-climbing, and especially by its most important development, the emancipation of the fore-limb. The story of the changes in the method of respiration is a singularly complicated one, since it is so inextricably interwoven with the changes produced in other systems that its main thread is apt to be lost in the complications which occur in every chapter. The primitive air-breathing Vertebrates draw air into their lungs by creating a suction within the spaces inside their bodies, and this they do by drawing their ribs upwards and outwards towards their fore-limbs. They "heave" their chests forwards, as one would pull out one end of a concertina, and so suck air into the lungs within their body cavity.

Inspiration in these animals (tailed Amphibians and unspecialized Reptiles) is produced by muscles that pull the ribs towards the fore-limbs; expiration by a reversal of the process, and by muscles which squeeze the internal cavity of the body and so drive the air out again.

In the most primitive of the Mammals a great change has come in, for the internal cavity of the body is sub-divided into a headward chest cavity, and a tailward abdominal cavity, and the lungs are separated from the abdominal viscera by a muscular partition—the dia-phragm. When the muscular diaphragm acts, it com-presses the abdominal cavity—this is its primitive function—but it can also create a suction in the chest by pulling its floor tailwards, or, to continue the simile, by pulling out the other end of the concertina. The diaphragm therefore becomes capable of assisting in drawing air into the lungs in inspiration.

There are, therefore, in the Mammals two possible mechanisms of inspiration; first, the original air-breathing vertebrate method of elevating the ribs to the shoulder girdle, and second, the new method of lowering the floor of the chest cavity. The one was named by Sir

Charles Bell the "external" and the other the "internal" respiratory system. It is possible for these two systems to be combined, and to act in consort. It is easy to realize that, with the action of the external respiratory system, a more effective inspiration will be produced if the internal respiratory system acts, even if it comes into place only in order to resist passive movement. In other words, the diaphragm must at least resist being sucked up into the chest during inspiration. This, for the most part, covers the range of activity of the diaphragm in the inspiration of most animals.

For the most advantageous functioning of the external respiratory system, it is necessary that the shoulder girdle and the fore-limb should be sufficiently fixed, at the moment of inspiration, to form a firm acting point for the muscles which pass from them to the ribs.

This is the condition present in the truly quadrupedal animals. In these animals the muscles which, arising from the fore-limbs and shoulder girdle, pass to the ribs pull the movable ribs towards the fixed limbs when they contract (see Fig. 49). A contracting muscle, however, is like a stretched elastic band; it pulls upon both of its attached ends, and will move that attachment which is least firmly fixed. In a quadrupedal animal, standing with its fore-limb firmly planted on the ground, the ribs are pulled to the relatively fixed fore-limb, but if the fore-limb be free and movable, it will be pulled towards the relatively fixed ribs. This is what actually happens in animals which have developed mobility of the fore-limb, at the expense of its stability. It reaches its climax in those animals which have completely emancipated the fore-limb, for in these animals the muscles of the external respiratory system have become muscles which produce added movements of the mobile fore-limb. The mobility and range of movements of the fore-limb are increased, but the efficiency of the primitive respiratory mechanism is impaired in proportion. It is now that the internal respiratory system becomes of increasing importance, and the animal of necessity begins to depend more and more upon its diaphragm as an inspiratory muscle (see Fig. 50).

We may say, therefore, that, as a general rule, pure quadrupedal animals use their external respiratory system

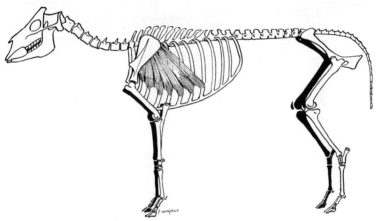

Fig. 49.—Diagram of a Quadrupedal Animal, to show the Muscles passing from the Relatively Fixed Fore-Limb to the Relatively Movable Ribs.

Only one muscle (serratus magnus) is represented. It produces elevation of the ribs and the inspiration of air.

most, but animals with emancipated fore-limbs depend more and more upon their internal respiratory system. So far is this the case, that in Man the original external respiratory muscles are almost universally regarded as no more than mere " extraordinary or accessory muscles of respiration."

It is perhaps worth turning aside to note how Man, when he needs added respiratory mechanism, attempts to take up a quadrupedal position, or at least change the mobility of his fore-limb back again to stability, in order to bring his primitive external respiratory muscles into play. A runner who is " blown " will grasp his

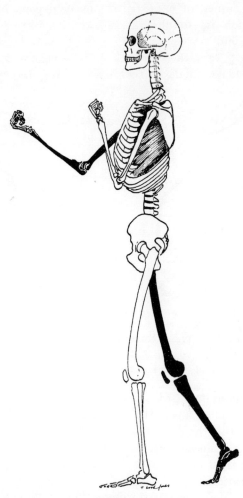

Fig. 50.—Diagram of a Human Skeleton, to show the Muscles passing from the Relatively Fixed Ribs to the Relatively Movable Fore-Limb.

Only one muscle (serratus magnus) is represented.   It produce1 a round arm-blow.

knees with his hands, and so fix his fore-limbs; a patient with embarrassed respiration will grasp the back of a chair, or adopt any convenient hold which may make him functionally a quadruped for the time being. Arboreal life has done this for the Primate stock—it has given them flat chests and flat backs, has brought about a greater degree of dependence upon the diaphragm as a mechanism of inspiration, and at the same time, has added to the mobile fore-limb an increased source of mobility in the muscles of the external respiratory system.

CHAPTER XXI

THE REPRODUCTIVE SYSTEM

THE influences of tree-climbing upon the reproductive habits, and consequently upon the reproductive system, are very great. They may be considered under two headings: as due to the arboreal life alone, or as they are outcomes of the emancipation of the fore-limb, which is itself a consequence of the arboreal life. The great factor involved under the first heading is the necessity for the reduction of the family in arboreal life. Arboreal animals tend to have small families, and some of the influences which have brought about this result are perfectly obvious. In the first place, large litters are, as a rule, produced among animals living such a life as affords rest and protection for the female during pregnancy. Pregnancy with a large litter and active arboreal life are almost incompatible. No matter what the underlying regulating factor may be, it is quite definitely in action, and although nest-building may offer a temporary expedient in a race of arboreal animals, reduction in the number of offspring produced at a birth will be the ultimate result. Again, apart altogether from the disabilities of pregnancy, there are the difficulties of dealing with large families when born to an arboreal mother. Helpless offspring in large numbers may be managed and cared for in some safe terrestrial nursery, but up a tree even were large numbers of such offspring produced, it is doubtful if many would survive. We know that the Tree Shrews build a nest, and so do some of the Lemurs (*Cheirogaleus*), as well as arboreal animals of other stocks, such as Rodents

138

(Squirrels and Dormice, etc.), Marsupials (*Phascologale*), and in the nest the offspring are nursed during their most helpless stage. But nest-building is only a temporary expedient in mammalian evolution, and reduction of the number of young produced at a birth is the ultimate outcome in a truly arboreal life. This is the result that has been arrived at in the Primate stock. The terrestrial Insectivora produce large families, *Centetes* even having a litter of twenty; *Tupaia* in its arboreal nest still begets three or four offspring at a birth. The family of the Marmosets very constantly numbers three. Among the Lemurs two young may be born at a time, and among all the Monkeys one offspring is the general rule, though two are not infrequently born.

Multiple pregnancies are, of course, primitive; and reduction of the family is acquired under the conditions of arboreal life. This reduction of the family produces its changes in the reproductive system. In the first place, the prenatal nidus designed to accommodate, say, twenty embryos may well be expected to show a structure anatomically different from one that is designed to accommodate a single embryo. In an animal in which the pregnancy is habitually multiple, the genital tract is divisible into three distinct parts (see Fig. 51). Leading from each ovary, from which the egg cells are shed, there are, on each side of the body, (1) thin tortuous tubes (the Falloppian tubes), which are merely ducts down which the egg cells pass into (2) the uterine cornua, which form the bilateral nidus in which the fertilized egg cells develop into the embryos; these two uterine cornua meet in (3) a small common median chamber, the body of the uterus, which opens into the vagina, and so to the exterior. In animals which have multiple offspring the embryos are developed in the uterine cornua. In *Centetes*, which we have already instanced, ten embryos might be expected in one cornu, and ten in the other. As the family becomes reduced so do the uterine cornua diminish, and the dwindling of the uterine cornua is harmonious with the diminishing family. Finally, when, in arboreal life, the begetting of a single offspring is the long-established habit, the cornua disappear altogether, and the single offspring is lodged in the single median

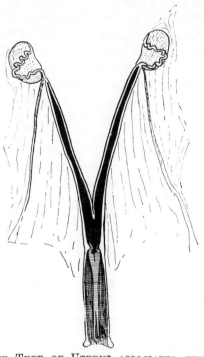

FIG. 51.—THE TYPE OF UTERUS ASSOCIATED WITH MULTIPLE PREGNANCIES. SMALL UTERINE CHAMBER, LARGE UTERINE CORNUA, SMALL FALLOPPIAN TUBES.

The diagram is taken from the uterus of the dog.

chamber—the uterine body. In the higher Primates, therefore, and in other typical arboreal animals such as the Sloths, the uterine cornua have practically disappeared, and the genital tract consists of (1) the Falloppian tubes, or egg ducts, leading into (3) the uterine body, which in turn opens to the vagina, and so to the exterior (see Fig. 52). A single median uterus for the accommodation of a single offspring is the outcome of the reduced family, typical of all perfected arboreal animals, and so typical of the Primates and Man.

The reduction of the family, and its final result in the production of only a single offspring at a birth, has had its effect also upon the development of the mammary glands. Mammary glands, as is well known, are serial

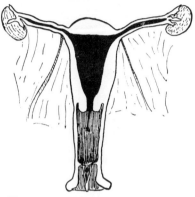

FIG. 52.—THE TYPE OF UTERUS ASSOCIATED WITH SINGLE PREGNANCY. LARGE UTERINE CHAMBER, NO UTERINE CORNUA, AND LARGE FALLOPPIAN TUBES.

The diagram is taken from the human uterus.

structures occurring upon a definite line—the mammary, or milk, line—which stretches from the axilla, along the sides of the chest and abdomen, over the inguinal region to the base of the tail (see Fig. 53). At intervals along this line mammary glands are developed in all the Eutherian mammals. The number of functional milk-secreting glands that are developed varies. In *Centetes*, whose large family we have already noted, twenty-two fully functioning glands—eleven on each side of the body —are developed. In the domestic sow the large mammary series is obvious and well known.

It is a general rule throughout the mammalian series

that the development of the mammary glands is in harmony with the number of offspring produced at a birth,

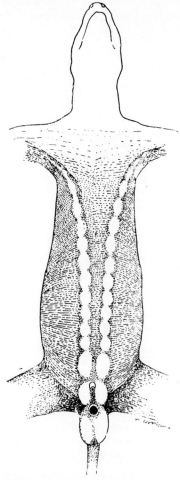

FIG. 53.—THE MAMMARY LINE UPON A HYPOTHETICAL MAMMAL, TO SHOW THE SITES AT WHICH MAMMARY GLANDS AND NIPPLES MAY BE DEVELOPED.

and so suckled simultaneously. Animals with large families possess multiple mammary glands for the suckling of the numerous offspring. With the reduction of the family, reduction of the mammary series takes place, and animals which produce few offspring at a birth possess few functional mammary glands. The manner of reduction of the mammary series in response to the lessened demands of a diminishing family is in no way haphazard, and, in a general way, it may be said that with a reduced family, those mammary glands are retained which are most convenient for the nursing of the offspring. If, in phylogeny, the family is reduced from ten to two, then instead of ten functional mammary glands persisting as the normal of the species, the number will probably be reduced to correspond to the diminished number of the offspring, and the glands selected for survival will be the pair at which it is most convenient for the mother to suckle the young. This convenience is ruled by the bodily habit and adaptations both of mother and offspring. It is here that the emancipation of the fore-limb enters as an important factor, for the infant is now enabled to grasp the mother, and the mother to grasp the infant. The young of the Lemur grasps tight to the mother's ventral fur, and in this way are carried about by her as she climbs among the branches. The method in which the young hangs on to the mother is curious, for while the mother is engaged in active climbing movements, the infant clings with its head towards the mother's tail. The legs encircle the mother's waist, and the hands grasp the hair of the mother's flanks, the infant's head being pressed against the inguinal region of the mother. The position taken up by the young is doubtless to permit of free arm movements on the part of the mother. Whilst in this position, the infant grasps in its mouth one member of a pair of inguinal nipples which are present in all Lemurs (and some Bats) (see Fig. 54). These inguinal nipples appear to be developed—or rather to persist— for a very definite reason, and they do not in the majority of cases convey any nourishment to the young, but merely serve to provide an extra hold for it during its mother's excursions about the branches. For this reason I have named them in a previous paper *the anchoring nipples*.

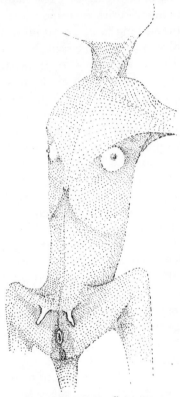

FIG. 54.—THE MAMMARY GLANDS OF A LEMUR.

The pectoral pair are functional organs, the inguinal pair serving only as anchoring nipples for the young.

Anchoring nipples are present in the Rhinolophid Bats, and have been named in these animals, by Rollinat and Trouessart, who have especially studied them, "faux tétons du pubis." In Bats the single offspring clings to these nipples during the mother's flight, just as the young Lemur clings whilst its mother climbs. These anchoring nipples are unassociated with milk secretory glands, but among the Marsupial animals the unusual circumstances of pouch life have led to the development of a peculiar type of nipple, which is both an anchoring and a milk-conveying nipple. Now, when the mother Lemur (or Bat) is at rest, the young one reverses

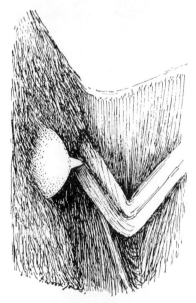

Fig. 55.—The Pectoral Mammary Gland of a Typical Bat (*Brachyphylla cavernarum*).

its position, and clinging with its legs round its mother's waist and grasping the fur of her chest with its hands, takes into its mouth one of a pair of pectoral nipples, and from this it suckles (see Figs. 55 and 56). The pectoral nipples are associated with pectoral mammary glands, and are the source of supply of infantile nutrition. The aberrant *Galeopithecus volans* probably combines the functions of milk secretion and of anchoring in its pectoral mammary glands (see Fig. 57). Now in the Primates higher than the Lemurs the inguinal anchoring nipples are

10

Fig. 56.—The Pectoral Mammary Gland of *Tarsius spectrum*.

There is another pair of nipples on the lower part of the abdominal wall.

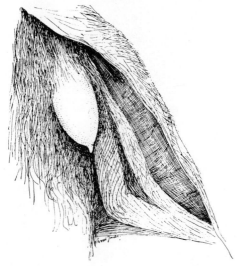

Fig. 57.—The Pectoral Mammary Gland of *Galeopithecus volans*, which is probably both a Milk-Secreting and an Anchoring Organ.

Fig. 58.—*Semnopithecus pileatus* (THE CAPPED LANGUR)
NURSING ITS OFFSPRING.

From a photograph by D. Seth Smith, Esq., taken in the Gardens
of the Zoological Society of London.

not developed (although as anomalies they may occur in so high a Primate as Man), and their disappearance becomes completed as the perfection of the emancipation of the fore-limb culminates in the power of the definitive hand grasp.

The young of Monkeys are held by their mothers, and they are nursed by their mothers, as Owen has described it, " in very human fashion "—the mother holds the offspring whilst it suckles at the pectoral mammary gland (see Fig 58). Lemurs do not hold and carry their offspring, but the offspring clings tight to the fur of the mother, and Charles Hose has observed that when *Tarsius* is called upon to pick up and carry her baby, she does it with her teeth, as cats commonly do. But all the Monkeys carry their babies, and hold them in their arms, nursing them " in very human fashion." When this stage is arrived at, the need for inguinal anchoring nipples is past, and the more convenient pectoral mammæ become the permanent Primate milk-secreting glands. The importance of the Primate ability to carry and nurse a baby cannot be over-estimated; many of its effects are produced very far beyond the limits of mere adaptations of the reproductive system and these effects will be considered elsewhere.

CHAPTER XXII

THE DEVELOPMENT OF THE BRAIN

It seems at first sight impossible to derive any advances in brain development from the mere habit of tree-climbing, and yet it is precisely these important and dominating advances which can most surely be linked up with the changing fortunes of the arboreal stock. Since any story of brain evolution is of necessity extremely complex, and since the different chapters in this story are interwoven in a very complicated manner, it is necessary to be quite certain of a tolerable degree of agreement about two things; the first, What sort of brain was that inherited by the earliest mammal? And the second, In what way will environmental possibilities of education affect such a brain? Fortunately, within rather wide limits, we may expect agreement upon these two points, and as the working basis of this review I shall take unreservedly the researches of Professor Elliot Smith. In that writer's paper on the " Origin of Mammals " the following statement occurs: " In spite of the certainty that the mammalian brain passed through a reptilian stage in its phylogeny, the brain of no living reptile fulfils the conditions required in the actual ancestor of the Protomammalia." Here we have evidently the same story, some of the pages of which we have turned previously. Somewhere, the Protomammal and the Primitive Reptile meet, somewhere in the geological past these two stocks branch off from a common ancestor. There is every reason to imagine that among the *Cynodontia* of the Triassic there was this blend of primitive Reptile and primitive Mammal which constitutes the ideal ancestor—the ancestor which possessed the ideal Proto-mammalian brain.

Although the brains of all existing Reptiles are too highly specialized, in one direction or another, in harmony with the specialized lives of their possessors, still it is to them, and to the much more lowly Dipnoi, that we must turn to obtain any concrete picture of the brain

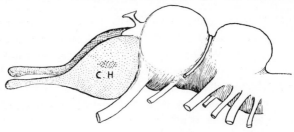

FIG. 59.—DIAGRAMMATIC OUTLINE OF A PRIMITIVE TYPE OF
VERTEBRATE BRAIN.

C.H., Cerebral hemisphere, practically all of which is devoted
to the sense of smell = archepallium. A small area, represented by coarser dots, indicates a portion of the cortex
connected with non-olfactory impressions.

of the earliest Mammal. The anatomical features need not be discussed in detail. Upon broad lines, such a brain consists of a collection of ganglionic masses, each mass definitely allotted to a particular sense or a particular function. To such a brain, impressions from special sense organs come by definite channels each to its definite anatomical station within the brain, and these central ganglionic stations are in free communication with each other. In addition to all this there is, as an outgrowth from each side of the brain, a small cerebral hemisphere, forerunner of the great cerebral cortex of the higher types (see Fig. 59). It is in these cerebral hemispheres that all the possibilities of evolution lie. It is the func-tion of the cortex that it provides an organ in which are blended the impressions that come by the several channels to the appropriate ganglionic masses—an organ in which impressions are sorted, associated, and stored, so that in the process such a complicated state as consciousness is evoked, and judgment and memory are made possible. Upon the completed cortex, complex pictures are woven and subsequently interwoven with others, and stored in that endless array of memories which constitutes experience, and forms the basis of judgments. But these things came slowly in evolution. The reflections from different centres and different channels found their way to the cortex gradually, and in definite order. First to obtain cerebral re-representation was the sense of *smell*, and this, of course, for the reason that smell impressions play such a predominant part in the life of a lowly animal. Placed right at the extreme fore-end of the primitive animal body, the great olfactory sense organs and the olfactory parts of the brain may be regarded as giving the animal its first impression of anything with which it came in contact. As the animal moved through life it tested and learned of life by this the most forward sense channel, and it was this which first demanded something more in brain development—it demanded a place in which to store up the impressions it was repeatedly gathering. The most primitive cerebral cortex is an olfactory cortex, and, following the nomenclature of Elliot Smith, we will term it the *Archepallium* (see Figs. 59 and 60). This, then, was the birthright of the Protomammal, a definite cerebral pallium, a small and limited storehouse, but a storehouse full of possibilities; for it was one in which impressions of one kind were already laid by ready for use at any time, to which others might conceivably find their way, and in which all might possibly be blended and retained in that intellectual medley comprised in memory and experience. Even in existing Reptiles some slight advance upon a pure olfactory cortex is seen, for " tactile paths have made their way into the hitherto almost exclusively olfactory cerebral hemispheres, and established some definite representation for the sense of touch in this dominant part of the brain " (Elliot Smith).

The slight advance made in the brains of existing Reptiles shows the initial stage of the attainment of the

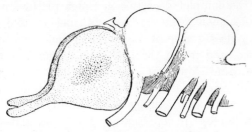

FIG. 60.—DIAGRAM OF A BRAIN IN A FURTHER STAGE OF EVO-
LUTION THAN THAT REPRESENTED IN FIG. 59.

The coarsely dotted, non-olfactory cortex or neopallium occupies
a larger portion of the cerebral hemisphere.

enormous possibilities which the possession of a cerebral pallium offered; but it was the uprising mammalian stock which took full advantage of all the possibilities (see Fig. 61).

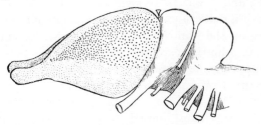

FIG. 61.—DIAGRAM OF A PRIMITIVE MAMMALIAN TYPE OF BRAIN
ILLUSTRATING THE RISE OF THE NEOPALLIUM (COARSELY
DOTTED AREA).

In the Mammal, not only do *smell* and *taste* impressions gain pallial representation, but impressions of *touch*, of *sight*, and of *hearing* streaming into the brain also demand their reflexion places in the receptive cerebral cortex. The originally small pallium becomes augmented by new areas for the reception, the blending, and the storage of these things, and these additions constitute what has been named by Elliot Smith the *Neopallium*. Following the same guide, we may therefore give comparatively simple answers to our two original questions: (1) The earliest Mammal inherited an archepallium capable of great achievements; (2) the environmental possibilities of education will affect such a brain by increasing elaborations of the neopallium, which the early Mammals started to develop.

How will arboreal life in particular influence this cerebral development ? For some aspects of this question we can again turn to the paper by Professor Elliot Smith to which we have already made reference, and the best introduction may be made in the form of a quotation:

" In the forerunners of the Mammalia the cerebral hemisphere was predominantly olfactory in function; and even when the true Mammal emerged, and all the other senses received due representation in the neopallium, the animal's behaviour was still influenced to a much greater extent by smell impressions than by those of the other senses. This was due not only to the fact that the sense of smell had already installed its instruments in, and taken possession of, the cerebral hemisphere, long before the advent in this dominant part of the brain of any adequate representation of the other senses, but also, and chiefly, because to a small land-grubbing animal the guidance of smell impressions, whether in search for food or as a means of recognition of friends or enemies, was much more serviceable than all the other senses. Thus the small creature's mental life was lived essentially in an atmosphere of odours, and every object in the outside world was judged primarily and predominantly by its smell: the sense of touch, vision, and hearing being merely auxiliary to the compelling influence of smell.

" Once such a creature left the solid earth and took to an aquatic or an arboreal life all this was changed, for away from the ground the guidance of the olfactory sense lost much of its usefulness; and in the case of aquatic Mammals, the whole smell apparatus atrophied, and in some cases vanished. We need not stop to consider the aquatic Mammal, because a life in the water calls for such marked specialization of structure that such creatures disappear from the race for mammalian supremacy. But the case is very different with arboreal Mammals. Life amidst the branches limits the usefulness of the olfactory organs."

So much seems evident; the only difficulty is for us, with our manifold channels of information, to realize how thoroughly the lowly terrestrial Vertebrates live their whole lives dominated by dependence upon the sense of smell. Friends, and food, are found by their scent, foes are avoided by the same sense, and the whole sexual life of the animal is lived in a like atmosphere. This is very largely the case even with the lowest Eutherian Mammals, and perhaps as familiar an example of the scent-dominated Mammal as can be chosen is the common English Shrew (*Sorex araneus*). In one feature this inquiry may be removed from the realms of the psychical into the domain of gross anatomy, and that altogether apart from a study of the structure of the brain. Scent glands of various kinds are most important anatomical features of these small and primitive Insectivora, and in them they reach a bewildering degree of complexity of development; but scent glands diminish steadily in those stocks which are truly arboreal. No trail of scent is laid among the branches of a tree, and for an animal that has become truly arboreal these glands are comparatively useless structures. In the tree-haunting Insectivora they have diminished, the anal glands being their last survivals. " In *Chiromys* and some other Lemuridæ the anal glands are reduced to two shallow cutaneous pits at the sides and upper part of the vent: in the higher Quadrumana this trace disappears " (Owen).

In the olfactory parts of the brain, and in the sensory

olfactory apparatus itself, the atrophy in the arboreal stock is extremely well marked, and smell impressions play but little part in the more important rôles in the lives of the Primates. In Man the sense of smell, and

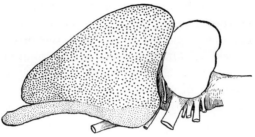

FIG. 62.—DIAGRAM OF A TYPICAL MAMMALIAN FORM OF BRAIN IN WHICH THE NEOPALLIUM HAS EXPANDED AT THE EXPENSE OF THE ARCHEPALLIUM (FINELY DOTTED AREA), AND OCCUPIES THE GREATER PART OF THE LATERAL PORTION OF THE CEREBRAL HEMISPHERE

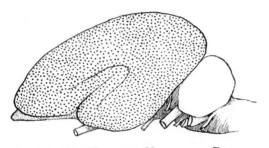

FIG. 63.—THE FINISHED MAMMALIAN BRAIN.

Diagram showing the general expansion of the cerebral hemisphere (neopallium), upon which fissures are beginning to appear. The archepallium is represented only by an inconsiderable (finely dotted) margin of cortex.

what may be termed the smell-life, are very minor factors in the whole physiological economy (see Figs. 62 and 63).

Nevertheless, this early sense which first gained a pallial representation, and became the first subject of memories and experiences, still shows in Man a subtle power as a memory sense. Dudley Kidd has noted this feature in investigating the psychology of Kafir children. " When Kafirs are questioned as to their earliest remembered impressions they usually state that these were connected with the senses of taste and smell. The next things they remember are connected with the sense of colour; then impressions of sound and of form seem to follow last of all." In still more primitive races the importance of smell impressions is probably greater; and there are few of us who have not some complex memory picture associated with an early impression of smell.

CHAPTER XXIII

THE STORY OF TACTILE IMPRESSIONS

IN picturing the activities of a primitive Mammal we have seen how large a share the sense of smell takes in regulating the life of the animal, and in guiding it about its habitat. A primitive Mammal may be said to " nose " its way about the world, and it " noses " its path through life in more senses than one   Just as its nose leads the way, and gives the first impression of novel objects by permitting the animal to become acquainted with their scent, so it gives the second impression of them by imparting to the animal a knowledge of their " feel." Such an animal is guided to an object by olfactory stimuli from the nose; afterwards, it tests the object with its snout.   This is a form of activity well seen among the Shrews; tactile impressions of everything with which they come into contact being conveyed by the elongated snout.   Touch tests for novel objects are carried on by the extreme anterior end of the animal body in all lower forms of life, and long before a " nose " is developed the animal is guided through life by touching those objects with which the fore-end of its moving body comes into contact.   When a definite nose is present, an animal may be said to learn tactile experience of its surroundings by bumping its nose into them.   In the lower Mammals this function is very obvious, and the anatomical adaptations to subserve it are numerous.   The snout region has set apart for its special innervation that great ganglionated cranial nerve known as the *trigeminal*, the branches of which convey sensory impulses from the whole of the skin area which surrounds the muzzle.   Moreover, special tactile sense organs are lodged in the skin of this region, and special tactile sensory hairs—the whiskers, etc.—are connected with them. When a Shrew, nosing its way about its habitat, comes across a novel object it learns much of it by its smell; but by the multiple stimuli imparted to the tactile sense organs, through the whiskers of its elongated and mobile muzzle, it considerably reinforces this knowledge, by adding an idea of size, form, etc., of the object, the smell of which has been tested. Snout-tactile, or fifth cranial nerve, impressions, therefore, soon find their way to the pallium, and the long muzzle becomes typical and emblematic of this association in all primitive Mammals, Prototherian, Metatherian, or Eutherian.

In dealing with the story of the fore-limb, we have seen what is the fate of this elongated snout in the evolution of the arboreal animals. With the emancipation of the fore-limb, and the development of the power of hand-grasp, there is seen harmonious recession of the snout region, the grasping hand taking on the functions of the grasping jaws.

But there is something more important and far-reaching than this in the process, for the grasping hand becomes also the *testing* and *touching* hand. Not only does the hand come to take over the crude grasping functions of the teeth and jaws, but in gradual stages it slowly but surely usurps the delicate tactile duties of the muzzle. The recession of the snout is therefore a vastly important thing, for not only are the characters of the jaws and teeth and the general build of the face profoundly altered, but the principal tactile organ of the animal body is transferred, as a whole, from one part to another. The liberated hand takes on the duties of the snout, and the exchange is effected very completely and harmoniously, so that all those functions formerly discharged by the snout are now carried on, and with far greater efficiency, by the hand.

The physical changes are great and obvious, but as possibilities of progress in evolution they are trivial, compared with the new avenues opened up for cerebral development.

The enormous difference which the translation of the receptive mechanism for touch impressions makes in animal economy is difficult to appreciate. Change of conduct, however, makes apparent the more striking lines of progress. The picture of the lowly animal which noses its way through life smelling with its nose, and examining with its snout all novel objects with which it comes in contact, is familiar to everyone, and is one that contrasts strongly with the behaviour of an animal that has become arboreal. Although it is a very long step to take, much may be learned by going straight to a Lemur and watching its treatment of novel objects. Here, handling obviously takes the place of nosing, although the scent test is by no means omitted, especially in all cases where the suitability of the object as an article of food is concerned. If *Nycticebus* is given some fruit which is new to it, it will examine the fruit with its fingers, pick it up with its hands if it be small, and then, as a rule, it will hold it to its nose. It will also smell its hands, and if these tests produce no result, some animals will proceed to rub the fruit, or hammer it on the ground, in order to obtain the scent from a bruised or scraped surface. All this is done before any attempt is made to eat any unfamiliar object. Much the same behaviour is shown when the animal tests an object which is merely a novelty, and is not regarded as a possible article of food. The superiority of hand-tactile information is at once seen by watching such an animal, and the possibilities of education of this new touch organ are easily realized. Even before the power of grasp is developed, we may imagine the dawn stages of educational advances initiated by hand touch. In the first place, the mere physical separation of the most

important tactile organ from the seat of the nasal scent impressions is important, for other things than those smelled
out or bumped into come constantly under examination.

The evolution is evidently harmonious in its details.
The more the fore-limb becomes emancipated, the less
is the hand called upon for menial duties which in other
stocks necessitate the development of skin thickenings,
pads, callosities, or hoofs. It is the freed hand which is
permitted to become the sensitive hand, and it is the
freed and sensitive hand which now, so to speak, goes in
advance of the animal and feels its way as it climbs
through life. The animal no longer smells out an object,
subsequently to feel it with its nose; but it feels with its
hand some object which comes within its reach in the
ordinary course of its arboreal activities, and it may or
may not subsequently add to its knowledge of the object
by smelling it. Tactile impressions gained through the
hand are therefore perpetually streaming into the brain
of an arboreal animal, and new avenues of learning about
its surroundings are being opened up as additions to the
old olfactory and snout-tactile routes. With the development of the power of grasp, new and great possibilities
come in. Much may be learned of an object that can be
felt by the hand; much more of an object that may be
grasped, lifted and examined in the hands. When an
object can be grasped and lifted it can be examined from
every point of view, and the eyes must play a large part
in this examination. Its whole outline, the texture of
its surface, its hardness or softness, its size, temperature,
and weight, can all be ascertained. It is difficult for
us, with our perfected cerebration, to appreciate the
difference which the power to grasp an object makes to an
animal attempting to learn the nature of objects with
which it comes in contact, but we may be sure that the
difference was very great, and was made greater when
the power to pick up the object and to examine it from
all points of view was added.

There are many other ramifications, and many other possibilities, of this educational gain in the possession of a sensitive tactile hand; there are the enormous advantages of the opportunities of correlating and checking impressions gained by other channels; the encouragement of the development of fine movements of the hands; the ultimate possibility of using in the hand an object judged to be useful (as a weapon or implement) by the hand; and a host of others. These we will not discuss here, but will leave for treatment, where their importance demands it, as separate entities.

CHAPTER XXIV

MOTOR IMPRESSIONS

THE very fact that the sense of touch becomes lodged, to so large an extent, in the emancipated hand of the arboreal animal becomes a guarantee that this hand will be called upon to discharge its tactile function in a variety of ways. All sorts of uses, previously quite foreign to it, will be demanded of it in virtue of its possibilities as a tactile organ. The combination of the increasing tactile perceptions, and the freedom of movement, creates a condition which ultimately leads to the most important developments.

The sensory stimuli streaming from the hand towards the central nervous system must become associated in the most intimate way with the motor impulses streaming to the mobile fingers. There is, in the end result, no gross alteration of the mechanism of the hand, but there is an enormous alteration in the nervous control over the hand, and the purposive skill with which it can be used. The hand, as a strangely primitive anatomical structure, becomes applied to all the finer and more skilful movements which the life necessities of the animal can demand of it. Every increase in cerebral development will make new demands upon it, and these demands are met by an increase of range of controlled, co-ordinated, fine movements. To those who, in the literature of a bygone age, were termed the " curious " it will appeal as an interesting theme that this hand, anatomically one of the most primitive parts of Man's body, one to be so nearly matched among the " hands " of the lowest

imbed Vertebrates, has responded to all the exacting
calls made upon its functions by the myriad promptings
of the complex human brain. We will, however, not
pursue this theme.

It is the necessity for the close association of the functions of sensation and mobility, which are subserved by
the emancipated hand, that is of interest in evolution
from the dawn stage we have pictured. We are concerned only with the problem of the possible manner in
which these things have affected brain development.
In the present state of knowledge this problem is a highly
complex one, but there can be no doubt that, on broad
lines, fairly simple underlying processes act harmoniously
in the evolution of the brain. There has been enunciated,
by Dr. Ariens Kappers, of Amsterdam, a theory of one
such underlying principle to which he has given the name
of " *neurobiotaxis.*" Put into simple language, the principle involved is a calling of the nervous seat of origin
of the outgoing motor impulses towards the site to which
the associated incoming sensory impulses stream. Suppose, for instance, the primitive nervous centre which is
associated with any definite sensibility to have a well-
defined anatomical position in the central nervous
system, then, in its immediate neighbourhood, and
attracted to it, will be the motor centre which governs
the movements of the parts most intimately related to
this particular sensibility. It may be that this particular
sensibility is intimately related to different movable parts
in different animals, and then in each will be found a
different motor centre appropriately attracted into the
closest anatomical relation to the sensory centre. This
general principle has been shown by Ariens Kappers to
hold good in the case of the ganglionic centres of the
cranial nerves, and to account for their otherwise inex-
plicable positions in the brain stem. This principle of
neurobiotaxis is, I believe, capable of extension from
the ganglionic masses in the brain stem, where Ariens

Kappers demonstrated its reality, to the pallial areas in the cerebral cortex, where these ganglionic masses gain re-representation.

There is an order in cortical representation of functions which is probably brought about by the same agency as that which determines the order of the basal ganglionic masses. We have seen that the first function to gain a representation in the cortical pallium is the sense of smell, and we have pictured snout-tactile impressions as following in its train. It is therefore likely that the site of representation of these snout tactile impressions will be in that part of the pallium which is in the immediate proximity of the olfactory area. Likely, too, that the associated mouth sense of taste will be in its near neighbourhood. Further, since in the brain stem the motor centres are attracted to sensory ones, it is likely that a pallial area associated with snout movements will also be developed in the neighbourhood of these sensory areas. We should now have a brain the cortex of which consisted of an archepallial olfactory area, and grouped in its immediate neighbourhood in the developing neo-pallium areas devoted to the storing, sorting, and association of impressions of taste, snout sensations, and snout movements. So far, our outline of brain building has been upon purely hypothetical grounds, but we can pass from this stage to reality at any moment by examining such functional charts as have been made of simple mammalian brains (see Figs. 64, 65, 66, 67 and 68). In the chart of such an animal the rather large olfactory area, or archepallium, has as its immediate neighbours in the neopallium a taste area, and an associated area related to tongue movements; and a tactile area in which sensations from the snout are stored, with, as a forward extension of this, an area which, when stimulated, evokes snout movements. We have now imagined a further development in which the hand is added to the snout as a tactile sensory organ, and in which the co-ordinated fine movements of the hand are increasing in perfection. These things we are picturing as demanding pallial representation, and it is likely that the hand-tactile area will be added as a new neopallial area beyond that devoted to snout touch, and that its corresponding motor area will be attracted to it as a distal addition to the snout move-ment area. This, again, is a condition which passes from

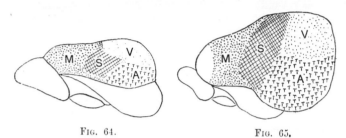

Fig. 64.   Fig. 65.

Fig. 64.—Cerebral Hemisphere of *Macroscelides* (the Jump-
    ing Shrew), to show the Cortical Areas as determined
    by Professor Elliot Smith. (From Duckworth.)
M, Motor.   S, Sensory.   V, visual.   A, auditory areas.   The
             white areas are olfactory.

Fig. 65.—Cerebral Hemisphere of *Tupaia* (the Tree Shrew),
    to show the Cortical Areas as determined by Pro-
    fessor Elliot Smith. (From Duckworth.)
Note the development of a prefrontal area in front of the motor
             cortex (M).

the hypothetical to the actual, for the sensory and motor association areas of the hand are laid down on the un-folding neopallium as outliers to those we have already seen to be realities.

For the present we will leave brain architecture at this point where neopallial representation is comprised, in our limited survey, to taste and tongue movement areas, snout tactile and snout movement areas; hand tactile and hand movement areas, as localized portions of cortex spreading from the old archepallial olfactory area over the unfolding neopallium. Meanwhile we will return to our arboreal animal to study the ever-increasing possibilities of its education.

The greatest difference between the process of gathering tactile impressions by the snout region, and receiving them by the hand, is that in the latter case the examination of a novel object is carried out to a far greater extent under the observation of the eyes. It is true that when

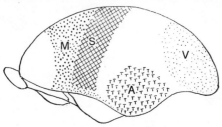

FIG. 66.—CEREBRAL HEMISPHERE OF *Tarsius spectrum*, TO SHOW THE CORTICAL AREAS AS DETERMINED BY PROFESSOR ELLIOT SMITH. (FROM DUCKWORTH.)

Note the development of intervening "association" areas between the visual (V), sensory (S), and auditory (A) fields, as well as the enlargement of the prefrontal area.

the snout region is the tactile organ, the object tested is brought into greater proximity with the eyes; but it is exposed to a far more limited and restricted view than when it is examined by the hand. Tactile impressions from the examining hand become correlated with visual impressions as simultaneous observations. Visual sensations will gain an added possibility as avenues of education, and their pallial representation will, in all probability, be augmented.

Again, two other factors must be added as affording paths by which education may advance. These two factors at first sight seem obscure, and possibly trivial, and yet it is not at all improbable that they have had marked effects upon cortical development. In the first place the emancipated hand may feel, examine, and test practically every part of the external surface of the body, and an animal may now treat its own body as a novel object and learn all about it. In the second place (as a result of the altered poise of the head, etc.) the eyes may also examine almost all of the body, and the animal then has a picture of its own external anatomy—a picture more perfect for some parts than for others. These two factors are correlated by the simultaneous observations of hand and eye, just as are the impressions gained by the examination of any object such as a nut or a grass-hopper. The meaning of this may perhaps be made more clear by taking examples. Some animals must of neces-sity possess an extremely limited knowledge of their own bodies. A tapir, for example, can see but little of its body, and can examine with its tactile nose only a very limited portion of it. An elephant would know next to nothing of its general form were it not enabled to gather touch impressions of those parts of its body accessible to its trunk. A horse can reach and touch a limited area with its nose, and can gather impressions in this way, and supplement these impressions by those gathered by its eyes. A dog can touch with its nose a wide area of its body, and can bring a great deal of it under the observation of its eyes. A very great advance is seen in any arboreal animal which possesses an emancipated fore-limb and a mobile head; there is little that a monkey does not know about its own external anatomy.

An arboreal animal gains a precise knowledge of its own body; it can realize its form, and it has, to a certain extent, a working idea of the alterations in its form which are the outcomes of the movements of its several parts.

I imagine that it is mostly in this way that the whole of the body gains cortical representation in the neopallium in ordered sequence, from nose to perineum. The cortical area in which this representation is localized is, as we should expect, an extension of the tactile nose and hand area in the developing neopallium. Some difficulty has always been felt in defining the qualities represented in this area. It could be conceived that there might be separated sensory and motor areas adjoining each other, or the two might be combined in one complex sensori-motor area, which, in the hope of providing a rather wider connotation, has been named the "*kinœsthetic area.*" Some of the difficulties would, I believe, be removed by naming it the "*pictured movement area,*" and for "pictured" we might substitute the words "realized" or "known," provided the connotation of

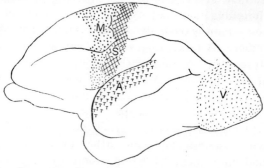

Fig. 67.—Cerebral Hemisphere of a Lemur, to show the Cortical Areas as determined by Brodmann. (From Duckworth.)

Note the general enlargement of the "association" areas from the stage seen in Tarsius.

these words were clearly understood. In this area are represented the impressions of those parts of the body of which the animal has concrete knowledge. The hand, the forearm, the elbow-joint, the arm, the shoulder; the trunk, the thigh, hip, knee, leg, ankle, foot, and perineum, all have their specially allotted areas in Man. And to these centres of the impression of pictured parts are added, possibly by the agency implied by neurobio-taxis, the centres concerned with the pictured movements of these parts.

Without an extended discussion of the anatomical details of the central nervous system, we may fall back

upon the axiom—agreed to by physiologists, patho-
logists, and anatomists—that "*movements, not muscles,
are represented in the cerebral cortex.*" I think we might
extend this axiom by claiming that only "pictured
movements" are represented in the cortex.

This axiom in reality teaches a great deal, for the brain
knows nothing of muscles, since the animal is itself
ignorant; but for movements it has a vast storehouse,
the contents of which are in direct ratio to the animal's
own pictured knowledge of the form and movements of
the different parts of its body.

We may gain considerable knowledge of the functions
of this pictured movement area by the consideration of
the results of experiments, which have been carried out
by different investigators, upon a series of animals of
varying zoological position. The movements of the
different parts of the body are not carried out in all
animals by the same nervous centres. We will tabulate
the experimental findings in order.

1. If a bird, or a Vertebrate lower than a bird, be
deprived of its brain altogether, it can continue the
movements of its limbs; a decapitated fowl is not a
paralyzed fowl, for it will continue to run and flap its
wings for some time despite the entire loss of its brain.
" It is possible to remove the entire cerebrum of a pigeon,
yet it is capable of flight when thrown into the air an
hour later " (Kinnier Wilson).

2. With a Mammal there is no activity, at all comparable to this manifestation, in the absence of a brain, but
very varying effects are produced in different Mammals
by removal of the pictured movement area of the cortex.

3. " On the day of removal of the cerebral centres for the
limbs, a rabbit will jump vigorously " (Kinnier Wilson).

4. If this area is removed in a puppy it does not become
paralyzed, and one week afterwards, when it has recovered
from the operation, it can carry out all the movements
proper to a normal dog.

5. With a monkey the effects of removal of the pictured movement area are much more grave, for the animal is very considerably damaged by the operation. It is not completely, but it is partially paralyzed, and the paralysis affects the hand movements far more than the leg movements. There is still, however, a very well-marked capacity for recovery.

6. In Man the effects of injury to, or disease of, this area, or of the fibres coming from the area, are very well known, and a Man whose pictured movement area is entirely destroyed is completely paralyzed on one side of his body. Moreover this paralysis is permanent. This unilateral paralysis, or hemiplegia, is of a very special type (upper neurone type), for the muscles themselves are perfectly capable of acting, are perfectly well nourished, and in a good state of tone; but their movements cannot be initiated for any pictured movement. Now, in connection with this upper neurone type of paralysis, there is one strange clinical fact which may be expressed in the usual axiomatic manner, by saying that " *a muscle which can perform two movements may be paralyzed for one movement, and not for the other.*" One pictured movement centre may be damaged, while a neighbouring one may be spared, and the muscle is only deprived of its power to take part in one of its previously possible movements. But more interesting still are those cases in which a muscle is entirely paralyzed for all pictured movements by the destruction of these areas, for then the muscle may still act, provided it plays some part in any movement which is not represented in the pictured movement area.

For example, a muscle (M. trapezius) which acts upon the shoulder and arm, and also upon the ribs, may be quite unable to perform its pictured movements upon the shoulder and the arm, after such a lesion (hemiplegia), but is quite competent to act when the patient labours in respiration, coughs, or sneezes, these movements not being represented in the pictured movement area. So much for some of the facts; what is the probable interpretation of them ?

It is obvious that in birds, and vertebrates lower than birds, there is a co-ordinating mechanism in the spinal cord—a reflex mechanism—which is capable of carrying on the movements of the body in the entire absence of the brain; that the brain is not necessary for the working of this reflex mechanism. In the rabbit and dog this reflex mechanism of the cord is considerably lessened, and the centre for the initiation of movement is in the brain; but it is obviously not (in its essential part) in the cortical pictured movement area. As a matter of fact, experimental evidence has proved it to be in a ganglionic mass connected with the cortical neopallium which is named the *corpus striatum* (for details see the work of Kinnier Wilson and others).

In a Monkey, although some movement is, without doubt, still initiated from the corpus striatum, much (and quite a definite part) is now lodged in the cortical pictured movement area.

In Man all the pictured movements are initiated from this area, but movements of which the individual has no definite pictured cognizance—such as the movements of the heart and viscera, and the movements of respiration —are still lodged in the ganglionic masses of the brain stem.

It would seem probable that the representation of the pictured movements are arranged in the neopallial cortex in a perfectly definite order, and that the sequence of their establishment is evidenced by the well-known distribution of the areas in the kinæsthetic region of the human brain (see Fig. 71, p. 192). It is perhaps not beyond possibility that the full lodgment of all pictured movements is not yet permanently effected in all human brains, and that the process is still in progress. There is certain anatomical support for such a supposition, but its exact nature does not concern us here, and we may rest content with the usual clinical conclusion that the lodgment has been so complete that damage of the whole of this kinæsthetic area causes a total inability to perform all " voluntary " —or more accurately—" pictured " movements. It should be noted that, although in popular usage it is commonly assumed that such oft-repeated things as the movements of the legs and feet in walking become " reflex," such an expression is totally inaccurate. No repetitive pictured movement ever becomes reflex in the sense that it is initiated anywhere than in the cortex of the neopallium. Its site of initiation is lodged in the neopallium, and it cannot be substituted by any " lower " centre. Were walking, for instance, ever to be performed as a true reflex, the power to walk would still be present in cases of hemiplegia. It is this complete translation of the initiating centre to the cortex which demands an education of the human motor functions. A human baby has to *learn* to walk, it has to learn all purposive pictured movements. The newborn young of a lower Mammal does not have to pass through the probationary period necessary to an animal, in which such movement is represented only in the cortex. There is a gradual scale in this feature displayed in the mammalian series, and to this we shall have to return in a subsequent chapter, since it is concerned with the problem of infancy.

From the point of view of cortical representation of motor impressions the arboreal habit has therefore probably effected a great deal. It has permitted of hand-testing, and it has enabled this testing to comprise a correlated study by the hands and the eyes. It has given scope for a wide range of fine hand movements, and it has demanded a high degree of co-ordination of these movements. It has also called forth a very special co-ordination of movements in the balancing, necessary in an arboreal life. And it has permitted the animal to know, and to picture, all the outward features of its bodily activities. All this has demanded cortical representation in the developing neopallium and has effected a translation (in which probably the principle of neuro biotaxis is involved) of the motor centres from a basal ganglionic mass into the kinæsthetic, or pictured, movement area. So far as I know, no human being, be he anatomist, physiologist, or clinician, has yet conceived so concrete a picture of the visceral movements involved in respiration, circulation, and the processes of alimentation, carried out in his own body, as to insure these movements a representation in his own cerebral cortex. And it is well that it is not so, for in that case the physician's attendance would be in more frequent demand, and hemiplegia would be inevitably fatal.

CHAPTER XXV

IMPRESSIONS OF SIGHT AND HEARING

THE two other senses, sight and hearing, which gain an early neopallial representation in the Mammals become of enhanced value to the arboreal animal. Their increasing importance in this stock is, in the first place, largely the outcome of the diminishing dominance of the sense of smell. When an animal ceases to find its way about the world guided almost entirely by olfactory impressions it begins to rely more and more upon other senses for its guidance. It is not that the sense of smell or its pallial representation becomes lost, but it ceases to be the main channel through which the animal gains knowledge of its surroundings. Sight, especially, becomes the principal guiding sense of the arboreal animal.

Both visual and auditory neopallial areas are well developed in terrestrial Mammals. There is nothing whatever distinctive of arboreal life in the mere cortical representation of these senses, but the arboreal life has a very definite influence upon the development of these areas.

Two essentially physical factors come prominently into play in the elaboration of the neopallial areas devoted to sight and hearing in arboreal animals. The first is one to which reference has been already made, and which may be termed the increased mobility of the poise of the head. There are obvious educational possibilities for the animal which can turn head and eyes and ears all together, and with the greatest rapidity, towards any object which attracts its attention by any sensory channel.

174

Then, again, there is that process which we have termed the recession of the snout region, which effects so many changes, and among them brings the two eyes to the front of the face. This purely physical change produces great and new possibilities of vision. In an animal in which the snout region is prolonged, the eyes are lateral, and the correlated vision of the two eyes is necessarily imperfect, each eye possessing a more or less independent

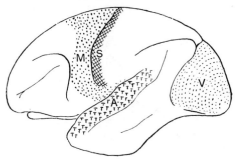

Fig. 68.—Cerebral Hemisphere of a Monkey (*Macacus*), to show the Cortical Areas as determined by Brodmann. (From Duckworth.)

A further advance is seen from the stage represented by the lemur, especially in the development of the prefrontal area.

field of vision; and the blending of the two visual fields into stereoscopic effects can be only very partially effected. There are, probably, not complete conditions of isolation of the two visual fields in Mammals, although among the Reptiles their complete separation is common enough, but the separation in many mammalian forms must approach completeness.

The power to look directly forwards with both eyes at once is present in all arboreal Mammals, but in many terrestrial quadrupedal pronogrades it is very limited. Even the dog is given to running with its head turned somewhat sideways, a position which, affecting the carriage of the whole of its body, is alternated at intervals

from side to side as the animal runs. When, with the
shortening of the face, the eyes are permanently brought
to the front, they both control one visual field. It is
noteworthy that in *Tarsius spectrum* the mobility of the
head seems almost to replace the mobility of the enormous
eyes, a change akin to that by which the mobility of the
head has already replaced the mobility of the ears (see
Fig. 70). Although in Man the two eyes see slightly

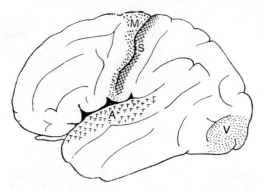

Fig. 69.—Human Cerebrum, to show the Main Cortical
Areas.

Note the general change in position of the areas with cortical
growth and also their wide separation by " association " areas.

different pictures when either is used alone, these pictures
overlap so greatly that with binocular vision they blend
into a common field in which stereoscopic effects are
produced. It is difficult to estimate the changes that this
has produced in the educational possibilities of the sense
of sight, but it is easy to realize that they have been great,
and I imagine it is to be appreciated crudely by studying
the different mental pictures produced by a simple photograph and stereoscopic views examined through the
appropriate lenses.

So far the arboreal animal has come to have a greater
dependence upon the impressions of sight and of hearing,
for the reason that its former guiding sense of smell is

Fig. 70.—An Adult Female *Tarsius spectrum.*
From a spirit specimen collected by Dr. Charles Hose in the
Baram District of Sarawak, Borneo.

12

now of only minor importance. It has increased the possibilities of both these senses by the greater mobility of its head, and, in the case of sight, by the recession of the snout region and the bringing of the eyes to the front. It is easy to see that these things can only increase the educational adaptability of these two senses, and add to the possibilities of the association of their impressions with (1) each other, and (2), in the case of sight, with the sense of touch.

This is exactly the condition which the neopallial development of arboreal animals would lead us to expect from pure anatomical and experimental evidences. When the auditory area is first laid down in the neopallium, it is situated at the hinder and lower portion of the cerebral hemisphere; the visual area lies immediately above it, and the kinæsthetic area lies in front of both. When the cerebral hemispheres expand with the increased demand for neopallial representation, the expansion does not take place equally. One portion of the cortex is in lateral apposition with the ganglionic mass of the corpus striatum, and this portion does not share in the expansion which affects those parts of the cerebral vesicle which have no such rigid anchoring mass in relation with them. This portion consequently remains more or less fixed (as the island of Reil), while the rest of the hollow hemispheres enlarge around it. As the cerebral hemispheres expand, the main direction of their growth is backwards, and in this way it comes about that the enlarging hollow hemispheres revolve round this fixed point as they grow (see Figs. 64–69).

The auditory portion of the neopallium, which was situated at the posterior inferior extremity of the primitive brain, grows downwards and forwards as it revolves below the island of Reil, pushed on from above by the enlarging visual field. Not only this, but, as it expands round the island of Reil, it becomes separated from the visual field by an intervening cortical area. The visual

field in its turn is pushed backwards by the expansion of
the neopallium, and so comes to occupy the posterior limit
of the cerebral hemisphere; and it, in its turn, becomes
separated from the sensory area by an intervening area
of cortex. An altogether new field, the prefrontal or
silent area, is developed at the anterior extremity of the
hemisphere, and it, by its growth and expansion, is largely
instrumental in bringing about the rotation around the
island of Reil, which has been described. In the brain
of a Lemur, and more markedly in the brain of a Monkey,
the original neopallial areas allotted to the several senses
have (1) migrated from before backwards round the
island of Reil as a centre, (2) have tended by their growth
to submerge this fixed field of cortex, and (3) have become
separated from each other by ever-widening fields of
intervening cortex (see Figs. 67 and 68). It is these
intervening areas, known as " association areas," which
are of interest. In them there is every reason to believe
that the impressions represented in the bounding areas
are blended and co-ordinated. It is these association
areas between the auditory and the visual, and between
the visual and the sensory fields which, enlarging in
the arboreal Primates, become the distinctive feature of
the human brain (see Fig. 69). And this anatomical
condition is the result we should expect from studying
the educational possibilities of the arboreal life.

CHAPTER XXVI

HIGHER DEVELOPMENTS OF CEREBRAL FUNCTIONS

It has often been assumed that the anatomist is incapable of making any real contribution towards the knowledge of the origin of Man, since he treats, and rather prides himself on treating, his material as though, to use Huxley's well-known expression, it were sent from some other planet, preserved, it may be, in a cask of rum. He takes cognizance only of muscles, bones, and other organs, but, it is urged there is something far more subtle than a mere assemblage of anatomical structures to be considered in the evolution of Man. Dwight, as an anatomist, has put forward this view with most cogency, but still, even when conducted with his skilful handling, and backed by his special knowledge, the argument cannot be considered as a reasonable one. Dwight has said that to regard an animal merely as an anatomical entity to which to assign a zoological position, " is a very narrow-minded and one-sided view to take of any organism, and, above all, of so high an organism as Man, whose intelligence (be its origin what you will) places him in an order of his own. The problem is of a higher sphere than that of morphology."

That the problem of the evolution of *intelligence* is beyond the reach of investigations undertaken in pure morphology is a proposition very difficult to combat when we are forced to take as objects for study " a bee or an ant or a wasp," such as Dwight postulates. But the difficulty is one imposed rather by the limitations of knowledge in the particular field selected, than by any

inherent inadequacy of a morphological method of study.
In dealing with the intelligence of Mammals the problem
becomes, in great measure, centred in the ascertainable
channels of cerebral education afforded by the several
senses, and the study of those educable fields of cerebral
cortex with which these senses are associated.   In this
way we may regard the intelligence of a Mammal as a
thing not wholly separated from its anatomical structure.
and therefore not wholly outside the province of, nor
entirely unexplained by, a purely morphological study.
Within the limits of knowledge, admittedly very imperfect, intelligence as a summation of cerebral possibilities
may be said to be a thing which falls within the province
of the anatomist; a thing concerning the evolution of
which he can glean some definite ideas by the methods
of comparative anatomy.   It becomes merely a question
of academic argument to deal with the next general
proposition as enunciated by Dwight: " Reason, involving
as it does general ideas, can by no possibility have been
evolved."   If we regard this formation of " general ideas "
merely as the product of a specially perfected type of
cerebral mechanism, a mechanism which we may see in
every stage of increasing perfection in existing forms,
then we are bound to admit that the faculty of reason
itself is merely an extension of evolutionary development
of the neopallium; and, indeed, there is no adequate
ground for doubting this.   Despite the pitfalls that may
occur over the use of mere words, " reason " is a product
of evolution just as much as is, say, the tactile association
area of the cerebral cortex.   Dwight's third proposition
that, " It is very evident that no process of survival
of the fittest could have led to higher ideals of conduct,"
is only likely to catch us tripping by the introduction of
the phrase " process of survival of the fittest " in place
of the previously used word " evolution."   The employ-
ment of this phrase is evidently not due to chance, since
it gives occasion for a picture, so easily drawn, of savage

nature, fierce struggles, and the consequent elimination of the weak, but possibly moral, individual, and all the other non-social tendencies, that the law of self-preservation in an active, possibly bloody, life-contest connotes. With this proposition we will deal further, leaving altogether untouched the fourth extension of Dwight's line of reasoning—" that the evolution of the soul is untenable as a scientific proposition."

For the present purposes we will take as our standpoint the thesis, that the rise of the neopallium is the tangible anatomical evidence of the perfection of cerebral processes, and that in the ordinary sequence of evolution the neopallial dominance and complexity culminate in the production of those faculties ordinarily connoted in the term " intelligence." An elaboration of intelligence, which we conceive to be simply attained in the ordinary workings of evolution, demands the rights of recognition as a more or less distinct faculty called " reason." It remains for us to ascertain if there is any indication in this evolution that an extension of the process along its normal lines could possibly lead to the formation of any basis for what is termed " higher ideals of conduct." It is necessary, first of all, to rid the problem of any suggestion that these things came about by a process of " survival of the fittest," in the sense that this survival means dominance in physical contest, in the elimination of the unfit in the sense of the physical weakling. There may be a much more peaceful evolution—but an evolution none the less—and I regard the arboreal life as a school in which some of the lessons of conduct were learned.

We have seen that arboreal life tends towards the reduction of the number of young produced at a birth, and that, in the Primate stock, it is the rule that but a single offspring is begot at each pregnancy. This, as I have pointed out in a previous chapter and elsewhere, is a mere adaptation to life circumstances—an application of the general rule that when no natural nursery is to hand there will be no large families. The roaming Ungulates, ready to flee upon the least apprehension of danger, have no natural nursery for their young, and in all of them the family is reduced. The pelagic Cetacea are in the same condition, and so also are the Sirenia.

Large families can only be indulged in by animals that can have a safe retreat in which to rear their numerous young, or by animals sufficiently equipped with weapons to guard them.

Of those animals which, having no nursery to hand, have a reduced litter, there are two distinct classes. The first class, for which we may turn to the horse (as a representative of the Ungulates) for an example, is made up of animals whose roaming life is composed of a series of escapes from danger; animals that depend for their safety, not upon their retreat into burrows, holes, or any other fastness open to some smaller beasts, but upon the swiftness of their open escape. These cannot be successful if the females are handicapped by the disabilities of pregnancy with large litters, or by the nursing of helpless offspring. In them the number of offspring is reduced, and the usually solitary infant is born singularly mature, so that it may share as soon as possible in the life-saving activities of its species.

The solitary young of such animals is born " grown up," it can flee at its mother's side within a few hours of its birth. Its period of dependence upon its mother is relatively short, and there is but little infancy, or childhood, for such a baby. In the second class come the arboreal animals. There is no natural nursery among the tree-tops, and the disabilities of pregnancy with a large litter are felt as keenly in active tree-climbers as in any class of animals. No doubt nest-building was resorted to as a temporary expedient in the arboreal stock; and among all the arboreal and semi-arboreal animals derived from many orders, nest-building, in some members, is still the rule. But nest-building only overcame a temporary disability, and in the end, reduction of the family solved the problem.

The baby of the perfectly adapted arboreal animals of the Primate stock is solitary; but it is a baby very different from that we have pictured in the previous group. The arboreal baby is born immature, and it is singularly dependent upon its mother in the precarious circumstances of life among the branches. There would seem to be no alternative in such a life; the baby must either be born a perfected tree-climber, or it must be a more or less immature creature dependent upon others for its safe conduct about the branches. As a matter of fact, the offspring of the Lemurs and Monkeys are born immature and comparatively helpless, save for the power of grasp which is well developed in their hands. Naturally they cannot immediately follow their mother upon her arboreal excursions; and among the Lemurs it is the rule for the young to grasp the mother, and among the Monkeys for the mother to assist by grasping the young. The Simian mother has to carry the baby with her wherever she goes; this, at the outset, is a new factor in the relation of mother and offspring. We may surmise that in this new relation there is given a wider scope for the working of that very primitive display of instinct summed up in the commonly used phrase "maternal care." Maternal care is, of course, perfectly well manifested in animals situated very differently from those we are studying; it is, in some of its manifestations, a widespread and primitive animal instinct. But the phrase "maternal care" when applied to a mother that, in time of danger, defends a dozen helpless offspring connotes something rather different from its extension to a mother that carries a solitary offspring which clings to her throughout a somewhat prolonged infancy.

It is to be regretted that observations upon the intimate details of the lives of the Primates in their natural state are not made more requently by those having the

opportunity to do so. Among the Lemurs, Charles Hose
has noted how *Tarsius* carries its baby in the way common
among cats, by picking it up with the teeth. It evidently
does not nurse its offspring.

The young of *Nycticebus tardigradus* clings tight to the
mother, and the mother makes but little effort to handle
its young. It will bite savagely if an attempt is made
to remove the baby from its fur, but, as a rule, it resents
any other interference in exactly the same manner. On
one occasion a female *Nycticebus* escaped from its cage
at night, and left its baby, which was still suckling, to
its fate. The baby, which was reared on the bottle,
used its voice freely each evening, but the mother, though
living in some trees quite close to its cage, never returned
to it. The voice of the mother was heard on rare occa-
sions, but five years passed before her actual home was
discovered; even then she was still within a few paces
of the spot in which she started her freedom, and in the
meanwhile the young one had died.

I do not know of any recorded observations which show
that in the Lemurs the maternal instinct is very much
developed beyond its display in carrying the helpless
baby clinging to the mother's fur. With Monkeys,
however, the care for the young is very real, and several
observations have been recorded upon this point. Both
in their natural state, and in captivity, Monkeys show
the greatest concern in the well-being of their offspring.
That they will defend them from attack is nothing, for
such a display of maternal instinct is the common property
of most living creatures, but Monkeys go further than
this in the development of those numerous tendernesses
for their young which in all accounts are, and can only
be, likened to human parallels.

With the Anthropoids, so far as opportunities for study
in their natural state have permitted, there is every
evidence that maternal and paternal care is carried still
further. Many observers have noted the human manner

in which the Gibbons attend to their young, and the
mothers have been seen to take their babies to the water
and carefully wash and dry them (Bock); even the
Gorilla has been seen to correct its offspring by boxing
its ears when it misbehaved (Koppenfels). Not only is
the display of maternal care much more marked in all
these higher arboreal Primates, but it is exercised for a
very much longer period than in any other animals.
Arboreal Primate babies have a very long babyhood and
a long infancy. The baby Gibbon (*Hylobates lar*) clings to
its mother for about seven months (Blanford), and it
is not fully mature until it is fourteen or fifteen years old
(Hartman). The young Orang-utan is dependent upon
its mother for about two years, and is not fully adult
until it is fifteen (Forbes).

This prolongation of infancy, and the period of youthful
dependence, has probably a rather widely reaching
influence. It calls for a much more prolonged exercise
of parental care and control, and causes these attributes
to be more or less permanent characteristics, rather than
periodically recurring manifestations of an instinct.
Again, the prolongation of infancy may be said to be
the especial factor which created the family as a social
unit. In almost all the higher Vertebrates it is the habit
of the male parent to remain with the mother during the
helpless early stages of the offspring, and in many instances (in several orders) he even plays his part in caring
for the young during their most dependent period. In
the Primates, the share that the male takes in the duties
of parenthood has often been noted. The males have
repeatedly been seen to carry the young on their arboreal
journeys, and it has even been asserted that the male
of the Siamang Gibbon (*Hylobates syndactylus*) always
carries the baby if it be a male, the female parent only
carrying a female offspring (Diard).

In whatever degree parental duties to the helpless
offspring are discharged by the male arboreal Primate,

it is evident he is only fulfilling a general biological law; but it also follows that if infantile helplessness is prolonged, his parental duties are liable to a similar extension. Here is evidently the beginning of that association of mother, father, and child which, lasting beyond a brief period comprised in courtship, the suckling of helpless young, and the guarding of mother and offspring, lays the foundation of the family.

When infancy is brief, the family bond is similarly of short duration; and, the period of suckling being ended, there comes a time of expansion of infantile enterprises, a time marked by some internecine strife and much parental intolerance. It becomes a necessity for the mother to repel the young when mammary activity is ended; it devolves upon the father to chastise any possible rivals: and in most large littered animals the family tie loosens and dissolves as soon as the young are fully capable of fending for themselves. As the period of dependence of the solitary offspring becomes more protracted, the advent of the dissolution of the family is naturally delayed—it may be delayed until the recurrence of the next natural parental sexual season. This I imagine to be a very important factor. If the bond of the helpless offspring keeps the male in attendance until the next sexual period of the female, there is likely to be a recurrence of the whole process, and a step towards the permanence of their union.

Although, as Professor Hickson has observed, there is a striking poverty of observations upon these very details of Primate economy, enough has been recorded to warrant some general statements. The Anthropoid Apes are met with almost invariably as family parties, or as solitary wandering individuals, and it is believed that pairing lasts for life. " The gorilla lives in a society consisting of male and female and their young of varying ages " (Koppenfels, quoted by Hartman). " The Chimpanzee either lives in separate families, or in small groups of families " (Hartman). " Each male lives with his own single female " (Forbes).

The Orang-utan—at any rate the male—seems to be rather more solitary, for he is generally encountered alone (Wallace), but " the female is generally accompanied by one of her progeny, sometimes by two, the one always an infant, and the other a more or less grown but immature individual of a previous birth " (Forbes). In the Gibbons is seen that amalgamation of families into groups which so frequently forms the basis of Monkey communities. There is room for very many more accurate observations upon the formation of these social communities, which, especially in the genus *Semnopithecus*, embrace a large number of individuals banded into an apparently fairly-well-defined group.

The Proboscis Monkey (*Nasalis larvatus*) lives in small communities embracing up to thirteen individuals (Hornaday); *Semnopithecus femoralis* in groups of from ten to thirty (Hose); with *S. cephaloterus* parties of from twenty to thirty (Tennant); and with *S. Barbii* from thirty to fifty (Anderson) are usual.

Most of the genus *Cercopithecus* live in communal groups which may contain from thirty to fifty individuals of such species as *C. campbelli* (Forbes). The Macaques also are group monkeys, *M. nemestrinus* sometimes forming considerable communities. The typical African Baboons live in extremely large packs, some companies being said to comprise as many as two thousand individuals (Slack), but these animals, being for the most part non-arboreal, do not so directly interest us.

The aberrant Black Baboon of the Celebes (*Cynopithecus niger*) is, however, an arboreal animal, and it is " usually seen in pairs, but sometimes a family of seven or eight may be found together feeding in a tree. Such families invariably consist of a pair of adults and a number of young ones " (Hickson). According to the natives these baboons pair for life.

Most of the New World Monkeys live in small communities, nevertheless the family unit is long maintained in some forms (*Lagothrix*, etc.), and in some is said to be permanent (*Pithecia*).

Amongst the Lemurs conditions vary greatly. Some live in small groups, but the majority remain isolated in pairs, or limited to family parties. Very little of the intimate details of their lives has been studied, but *Tarsius spectrum* definitely " lives in pairs " (Hose), and so does *Nycticebus tardigradus*.

If higher ideals of conduct are admitted to be mere extensions of a natural cerebral evolution of which so many other developments are certainly known, it will be under such conditions as those we have been picturing that they will be called into being. If higher ideals of conduct are to be acquired as an evolutionary process. it is in the family circle that their rudiments will be laid down, and it is in the family circle and in the society composed of families that these rudiments will be perfected.

CHAPTER XXVII

HIGHER DEVELOPMENTS OF CEREBRAL FUNCTIONS: POSSIBLE ANATOMICAL BASIS

When we come to make any attempt to attach a precise location to the neopallial representation of such higher cere bral developments as " intelligence " and " higher ideals of conduct," we are at once met with an overwhelming difficulty, a difficulty almost as great as that which con fronted the mediæval anatomists who sought a structural habitat for the " soul." The difficulties are so great, and imagination must play so large a part in attempting to overcome them, that very considerable latitude must be permitted in their treatment. It is, however, possible, and permissible, to make guesses, provided the guesses are carefully deprived of any pretence to be a part of, or take equal rank with, knowledge derived from ascertainable facts. It is for this reason that a discussion of an anatomical basis of " intelligence " and " higher ideals of conduct " is isolated from the study of those other things which an anatomist can, and must, investigate with scalpel and forceps. In the first place, I conceive that " intelligence," " reason," " intellect," the " mind," or any other word which has a like connotation, denotes a thing somewhat different from " higher ideals of conduct." It is not the most intellectual person who necessarily has the highest ideals of conduct I have regarded intelligence as an expression for the summation of the cerebral possibilities of an animal. The channels by which education can come to the cortex, the development of the cortical areas and their correlation and association, compose the physical basis of an animal's intelligence. It is even possible to conceive a creature in which neopallial development had reached its very highest point, in which channels of education were multiplied, and in which cortical areas were elaborated and associated in a bewildering complexity, culminating in the highest possible receptive, sorting, associating, and storing mechanism evidenced by a prodigy of intelligence or intellect, but in which higher ideals of conduct were absent.

If, then, we can imagine what constitutes the anatomical basis of intelligence, what picture have we of the physical seat of " higher ideals of conduct "? There is a well-known cortical area, which is situated at the anterior end of the neopallium, that has yielded up no secrets to the experimental investigator. It is called at times the " silent area," since stimulation of it produces no result in the ordinary methods of experiment; from its anatomical position, it is also named the " frontal " or " prefrontal " area. This portion of the brain is already beginning to differentiate in the Tree Shrews; it increases through the whole Primate stock, and is developed to its greatest extent in Man. We may regard the neopallial cortex as a mantle in which are situated receptive centres of different impressions, and we may regard the elaboration of the neopallium as a growth of " association areas " interposed between the areas allotted to these different impressions.

In " association areas " are blended impressions from different receptive centres, and in them are formed, sorted, and stored memories and experiences derived from the several senses, the centres for which march with their borders. This prefrontal region marches upon the borders of only one such area—the so-called " motor " area. If this prefrontal area be—as it is generally assumed to be—the seat of " memory, judgment, and imagination " or of " higher mental faculties, of co-

ordinated ideas," etc., it seems strange that its only
associated areas should be the "motor" centre (see Figs.
64–69, and 71). We have seen that there appears to be an
underlying functional order in the massing of the neopallial
areas, and it is therefore disconcerting to find this purely
ethical centre developed as an extension of, and associated
only with, the motor area. But we have already postu-

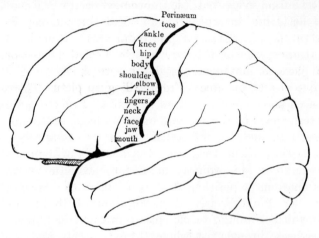

FIG. 71.—DIAGRAM OF THE LEFT CEREBRAL HEMISPHERE OF A
HUMAN BRAIN, TO SHOW THE ORDER OF REPRESENTATION
IN THE "PICTURED MOVEMENT" AREA.

lated that this so-called motor area is a field devoted to
a very special motor function which we have attempted
to express as "pictured movements." We are assuming
that it is an area in which are lodged impressions of the
movements of which the animal has present cognizance,
a function which may be crudely expressed by saying
that it comprises the movements which an animal can
see and feel itself doing. It is, therefore, not so improbable that this new anterior silent area, which has
connection with no other neopallial areas, is simply an
extension from this specialized pictured movement area,
and probably an association area of it. It is not im-

possible to imagine that an area which is an association or extension area of this field, in which an animal's actual pictured movements are stored and sorted, might be connected with a further elaboration—in the form of an idealization—of pictured movements. From a conception of a concrete movement performed under actual circumstances, it may be that passage is made to the idealization of a possible movement performed under hypothetical circumstances, and that this latter process takes place in the silent prefrontal area. Probably the first occupation of this new area is effected by memories of pictured movements, and the sorting of experiences gained by this source. From calling up pictures of past associations of pictured movements, there is perhaps a step towards constructing conceptions of future movements evoked by pictured hypothetical circumstances. The picturing of action in hypothetical circumstances seems to me to be almost synonymous with such a concept as conduct. Conduct can only be pictured in terms of action. We may say that in the gaining of this prefrontal neopallial area the animal passes from a state in which it has a conception of its present and actual movements to a state in which it has memories of past movements and pictured concepts of possible future movements. The animal without a neopallial kinæsthetic area performs all its actions in the absence of any pictured consciousness of the action. An animal with a kinæsthetic area performs actions of which it has a definite mental pictured conception. *It knows what it is doing.*

An animal with a developing prefrontal association area has, in addition, memories of its past actions. *It knows what it is doing, and it remembers what it has done.* An animal with an elaborated prefrontal area has, in addition, the faculty for building up pictures of possible future actions. *It knows what it is doing, it remembers what it has done, and it can estimate what it might do.* We may translate this into the phraseology usual in the

13

description of human mentality. That it knows what it is doing presupposes the existence of *consciousness*. That it remembers what it has done argues the dawning of a *conscience*. That it can estimate what it might do implies the laying of the foundation stone for building *ideals of conduct*. Here is at least the basis for the formation of that grade of moral social behaviour that results from the lessons taught by experience. If ideals of conduct be the answers to an ever-insistent series of problems comprised in the question, " What shall I do ?" then the area in which ideals of conduct are lodged is, very probably, the prefrontal silent area. It must be pointed out that in thus approaching the question of the function of this area we are proceeding by more or less logical steps; we are not merely localizing vague functions, of which we can obtain no physical signs, in an area from which no response can be elicited by experiment. We are not forced by the extremities which urged Descartes to assign the habitation of the soul to the pineal body, but we are attempting to determine the functions of this association area, just as we should determine the function of any such area, by ascertaining the probable characters of its neighbours.

But this finding brings us face to face with the difficulty, that in imagining the intellect to be represented anatomically in the summation of all the neopallial areas, and ideals of conduct to be lodged in the prefrontal areas, we are supposing a rather definite separation of these two factors in cortical representation. I believe that this is, as a matter of fact, no difficulty at all, but is in many ways a clue to understanding some normal and abnormal conditions displayed in human mentality. It should be possible to have a very definite separation of these qualities displayed by their very unequal development in different individuals. There are certainly persons in whom no very special qualities of the intellectual mind are present, but to whom the problems of conscience and conduct bulk so large as to be a definitely one-sided development. Again, there are others whose intellectual mind is particularly well developed, but whose conceptions of conduct and of conscience are distinctly below the average. Disease may apparently affect these two qualities separately, and I imagine that advances in knowledge are likely to be made only by attacking the problem along these lines.

The views of Charles Mercier have been vividly expressed to the medical profession, but apparently they have been but little comprehended. " Alienists still deny that insanity is disorder of conduct, though they witness such disorder in every case of insanity that comes before them; they still declare that disorder of mind is insanity, in the face of many mental disorders in which not a trace of insanity can be found " (Mercier). Most physicians are familiar with the patient whose abnormal conduct demands his confinement within the walls of an asylum, but whose intellect would be envied by many whose conduct fits them to live without those walls. Equally familiar is the patient whose intellectual estimation of the abnormalities of conduct displayed by his fellow-inmates is perfectly sound, but whose own conduct is possibly even more abnormal than that which he criticizes adversely in others. On the other hand, the conduct of an individual in whom damage of an association area prevents his intellectual mind from finding the least meaning in the spoken words of his fellow-men may be perfect.

Should reason and intelligence be the outcome of the perfection of cortical representations of the several senses and the development of ample association areas, and should the formation of higher ideals of conduct be a concomitant phenomenon dependent upon the development of a prefrontal association area, then the rise of these things may be followed (by the ordinary methods of the anatomist and physiologist) in the elaborating cerebral hemispheres of the arboreal stock, which culminates in Man.

CHAPTER XXVIII

THE BRAIN AND THE BODY

WE have seen that arboreal life may be regarded as offering opportunities for educational possibilities unknown in terrestrial life. We have also seen that it probably brings about certain bodily modifications. We are now confronted by a problem: Did the cerebral advance create the physical adaptations, or did the physical adaptations make possible a cerebral advance ? It would seem, at first sight, that upon such a problem the argument might be as long sustained, and as futile, as that expended upon the question of the priority of the hen or the egg. And yet the question is a very interesting one, and one well worthy of attention. It is certainly not to be dismissed by a series of confident and epigrammatic assertions. It is possible that at least a partial solution can be given.

Using a form of words wellnigh meaningless, but nevertheless well understood, we may say that Nature has made several experiments in brain-building. Vertebrate brains are not built all upon one plan; even within the limits of the Mammals, brain architecture varies considerably in basal design in the Prototheria (Monotremes), Metatheria (Marsupials), and Eutheria (higher Mammals). There is no living prototherian animal which has adopted the arboreal habit, and the few existing members of the Monotremes lead lives of particularly restricted possibilities. But many of the Metatheria lead lives as truly arboreal as that of any animal, and, indeed, the Marsupial stock is regarded by some as being primarily arboreal.

196

These arboreal Metatherians have had all the educational advantages of a thoroughly arboreal life; nothing that we have pictured has failed to exert its influences upon them, and yet it is obvious that the advantage that they have taken of it has been slight.   There are metatherian convergent mimics of Carnivora, Rodentia, Insectivora, and of most other Eutherian orders, but there is no metatherian convergent mimic of the eutherian Primates. It would not be unnatural, therefore, to assume that the full advantage could not be grasped by the metatherian animals, since the ground-plan of their brain would not permit it.   Climbing metatherians with perfectly mobile fore-limbs and grasping members were at one time classed, upon the strength of this feature, amongst the Cheiropeds, a group which included only them (*Didelphidæ*, etc.) and the Primates; but they were sorry companions for the Monkeys and the Lemurs in all other respects.   Life habit has made them physical mimics, in some degree, of the Eutherian Primates; it has not made them mimics in any cerebral feature.   Rotating forearms, grasping fingers, opposable thumbs—all these features are found in perfect combination in the arboreal metatherians, and yet far short of a human, no anthropoid, no simian, and no lemurine evolution is seen in the Metatheria.   Obviously, it is not the bodily adaptations alone that have sufficed to create the possibilities of Primate brain development.   We have followed the changes in physical advances and seen how these have affected Primate evolution, each physical adaptation leading to new possibilities of cerebral advance.   All these physical changes could be followed equally well in the Metatheria, but we should fail to note a corresponding advance in cerebral perfection.   It is, therefore, natural to ask if there is any gross condition of brain architecture which will serve to distinguish the metatherian from the eutherian brain, and if this distinction will in any way account for the very slight evolutionary advances made by thoroughly arboreal

metatherians. Anatomically, this question receives an
almost perfect answer. Without entering into a bewildering array of interesting anatomical details which, determined by Owen, were somewhat obscured by later
writers, only to be defined with more striking emphasis
by Elliot Smith and other recent workers, we may assume
that, on the whole, it was the development of the *corpus
callosum* and all its associated structures that gave the
eutherian brain its psychical as well as its anatomical
distinction (see Figs. 72 and 73). A true *corpus callosum*
—the great cross-connecting bond of the two neopallial
areas—is the outstanding feature of the eutherian brain,
and is the index of its neopallial perfection. Without
neopallial possibilities, educational advantages and physical perfections come in vain to the animal.

The evolution of the free and mobile fore-limb in
arboreal life may be likened to the production of a musical
instrument—an instrument upon which it is impossible
for the animal to produce a full range of harmony, or to
appreciate the psychical connotations of this harmony,
unless adequate cerebration is developed coincidently.

Once again in the evolutionary story we are forced
back to consider a combination of seemingly trivial, and
apparently chance, associations; in this case the dawning
possibilities of neopallial developments combined with
the physical adaptations due directly to environmental
influences.

Some authorities have ascribed great, and possibly
undue, influence to the changes in brain architecture,
while some have concentrated upon the purely bodily
adaptations. The solution of the problem lies probably
in the consideration of the mean of these two influences.
Physical perfections of adaptation are useless, unless
advantage can be taken of them by a specialized type of
brain; but specialization of the cerebral architecture
cannot proceed in the absence of, yet cannot create,
physical specializations in evolution. The earliest

Mammal possibly had the physical advance placed within its reach. The earliest eutherian Mammal

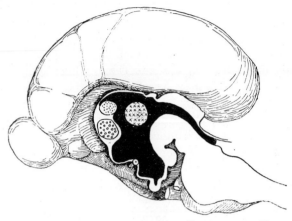

FIG. 72.—DIAGRAM TAKEN FROM THE DRAWING BY PROFESSOR G. ELLIOT SMITH OF THE BRAIN OF *Ornithorhynchus*.

The brain is in medial section and the commissures are cut across. There is no corpus callosum.

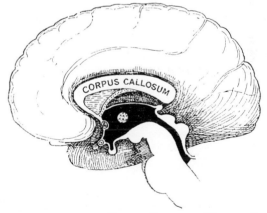

FIG. 73.—DIAGRAM OF THE HUMAN BRAIN IN MEDIAL SECTION.

The commissures are marked in a similar manner to those shown in Fig. 72. Note the size of the corpus callosum.

possessed the cerebral condition which made it possible for it to take full advantage of the physical advance.

Neopallial perfections did not, for instance, create the hand, but cerebral advances made possible the full utilization of this very primitive yet very plastic member.

Large-brained Man has invented schemes of classification which embrace all living things, and he has agreed that the brain perfection which he possesses is to be adjudged, in his schemes, as the qualification for the highest rank. We may therefore say that, from a human point of view, evolution consists of increasing perfection of the brain, and that an animal's place in the scale of Nature may be determined, in the last resort, by an appeal to its cerebral development. In this sense, the brain has led the way in evolution, and physical adaptations may be regarded as following in its train. Yet the physical adaptations are by no means to be ignored. A Master may perform marvels upon the violin, but his expression will be seriously hampered if there is nothing better to hand than an empty cigar-box strung with a few strings. Man may execute a bewildering array of highly skilled movements with his thumb and five fingers, but it is difficult to see how the human brain could have coped with a fore-limb in which stability had predominated in the culmination of a second segment devoid of the power of rotation and furnished with a terminal hoof.

CHAPTER XXIX

THE HUMAN BABY

IT is to the young of animals that we look, as a rule, to find evidences of the lingering of ancestral habits. Evidences of an ancestral arboreal habit might possibly linger under some guise or other in the young of an animal which, descended from an arboreal stock, has ceased to make its home among the branches.

A striking illustration of the converse of this expectation may perhaps make the argument more clear. Among the birds, the whole family of the Terns (*Sternidæ*) is characterized by a typically terrestrial habit of incubation, for their eggs are laid upon the bare ground. It is true that some species make a slight attempt at nest-building, and some meagre wisps are brought together to line a shallow depression in the beach shingle. In the case of one member of the family (*Anous stolidus*), this nest may rise, as a collection of sea-wrack, to the dignity of being a little mound; but the general rule is that the egg is laid bare upon the ground. The Tropic Island White Tern (*Gygis candida*) has, however, taken to an arboreal life, and it lays its solitary egg upon the branch of a tree. No nest whatever is constructed, and no attempt is made to insure the safety of the egg beyond selecting a spot upon a branch where some irregularity of the bark will prevent it freely rolling away. Although in this business of finding a suitable place, in balancing a naked egg upon a bare branch, and in the whole process of sitting upon this delicately poised egg, the adults show a very complete adaptation to their new surroundings, the offspring is hatched as an obviously terrestrial creature.

It is not so completely helpless as is the typical inhabitant of an arboreal nest, nor is it hatched perfected for arboreal life, but it exhibits just that ability for early terrestrial enterprise that the typical terrestrially hatched members of its family possess.

It is this retention of the old terrestrial adaptation of the young that causes a defect in this otherwise singularly successful assumption of arboreal habit, for the dangerous degree of ability in terrestrial enterprise, which the young still possesses, leads at times to its early destruction by falling from the branch. No doubt there are good reasons—probably in the shape of land-crabs and rats—for the adoption of this strange nesting habit by *Gygis candida*, but, even were there no typical Terns in which the ancestral customs could be studied, an examination of the young would at once reveal the fact that the parental arboreal life was a comparatively recent assumption by the species. As the baby White Tern shows so well its terrestrial inheritance, whilst its parents are so perfectly adapted to an arboreal life, it is not unlikely that the human baby will show its arboreal inheritance better than its terrestrially modified parent.

We will first turn to so obvious a point as the relative lengths of the arm and leg. In typical arboreal Primates the arm is longer than the leg, and in some forms, such as the Orang-utan, the disproportion is very well marked. This disproportion may be expressed by means of an " intermembral index," which, without further discussion, we may accept as an arithmetical expression of the relation of fore and hind limb lengths, which is high when the arm is relatively long, and low when it is relatively short. In the Orang-utan this index is about 140, in the Gorilla about 118, and in the Chimpanzee only 104. In adult Man the alteration has been so great that, though the index is as high as 83·6 for the Bambute Pygmies (Shrubshall), it averages no more than 67 in most Europeans (Duckworth).

But it is to be noted that the anthropoid proportions
are retained in the human fœtus until a relatively late
stage (see Figs. 74 and 75), and that even in the human
baby the proportion of arm length to leg length approaches the index of the Chimpanzee (see Fig. 76), the

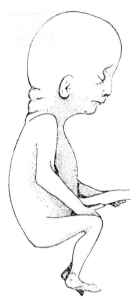

FIG. 74.—HUMAN EMBRYO
105 MM. IN TOTAL
LENGTH.

FIG. 75.—HUMAN EMBRYO
195 MM. IN TOTAL
LENGTH.

disproportionate growth of the human leg being largely
a post-natal development. At one stage of human
embryonic development the arm is longer than the leg
—a typically arboreal Primate feature; later the two
members are equal, and then the leg outstrips the arm
in relative growth. When the baby is born this human
lengthening of the leg proceeds more rapidly; when the
child begins to walk the disproportion becomes more
marked (see Fig. 77), and the influence of this factor is
marked until about the period of the fifteenth year of

life (see Fig. 78). This later human growth of the leg
may be expressed more crudely, but perhaps more
strikingly, in another way. When a baby is born, its
umbilicus is below the middle point of its entire body
length, measured from the soles of its feet to the crown

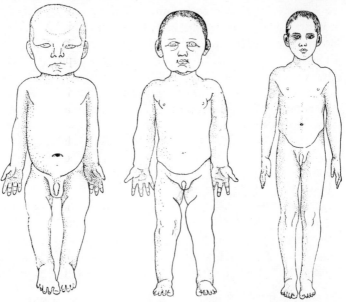

FIG. 76.—NEWBORN   FIG. 77.—CHILD EIGHTEEN   FIG. 78.—CHILD SIX
     BABY.   MONTHS OLD.   YEARS OLD.

of its head. But as the post-natal growth proceeds, the
umbilicus moves relatively upwards, and by the end of
the eighteenth month it is the central point of the body
length. By the fifteenth year it is well above this point,
which is now situated in the region of the pubic symphysis.
It is worthy of note that in this feature the male has
advanced more than the female, since the preponderant
growth of the legs has exerted a more marked influence
in displacing the body centre in the adult man than in
the adult woman.

In the relative proportion of arm and leg the human baby is, therefore, far more like an Anthropoid—far more like an arboreal animal—than are its parents.

In other features the same tendency is shown, and we will only note in passing the far greater power of toe-grasp displayed by infants and young children than is ever seen in European adults. This point is merely noted, and no stress is laid on it, since the habit of wearing boots is so readily appealed to as the factor which has deprived the adult European foot of its grasping powers. One other detail with regard to the foot of the human baby should be mentioned, and that is the inturning of the soles, which, characteristic of the arboreal Primates, is so well marked in infants. The soles of a baby's feet are turned inwards so completely that they can be pressed flat against each other, this, indeed, being a common position of rest in an infant, as in an arboreal Anthropoid.

When children learn to walk, it is upon the outer side of their feet that they trust their weight, exactly as the Anthropoids are wont to do. The bones upon the outer side of the feet are first ossified, and it is the outer margin of the foot which first bears the body weight; the eversion of the foot is a later and a human characteristic. It is this inherited arboreal foot-poise which leads children to make holes in the outer sides of the soles of their boots before the inner margin are subjected to any great degree of wearing.

Only one other arboreal characteristic of the human baby will be noted here, and that is one which has so often been discussed, as to be well within the bounds of homely and domestic knowledge. No one who has let even a very young baby entwine its fingers in his hair, or has permitted a slightly older one to grapple with his watch and chain, will doubt the very real power of an infant's hand-grasp. This extraordinary power of hand-grasp, although a very homely thing, is one of the most astonishing features of a newborn baby. It is generally known that a baby within an hour of its birth can support its body weight by hanging with its hands for at least ten seconds. One observer (Dr. Louis Robinson) has recorded the fact that twelve infants under one hour old supported themselves thus for thirty seconds, and that three or four could hold on for almost a minute. When the child is between a fortnight and a month old, it can support its body weight by its hands for a longer period, some even being capable of hanging on for two minutes, but after a month the baby generally refuses to be tried by any such test, and relaxes its grasp when any strain is exerted upon its arms.

The suspension of the body weight for even a minute by a baby a fortnight old may not seem to be a very astonishing feat, and yet it is quite as much as most adults can do. The suspension for two minutes thirty-five seconds which Dr. Louis Robinson records for a baby of three weeks is a truly remarkable performance, since it is longer than that possible for the average healthy schoolboy, and far longer than that attainable by most adults.

This curious strength of the grasp and of the arms is an obvious arboreal adaptation of the human baby. It is the survival of the grip which enabled it to cling to its mother, and to the branches of its arboreal home, and as such it wanes in the human body after the first few months of its life, and becomes still less when the power of walking upright is fully acquired in infancy.

CHAPTER XXX

THE ARBOREAL ACTIVITIES OF MODERN MAN

IF tree-climbing has done so much for the human stock, and if the arboreal habit is, so to speak, so near to the basis of humanity, it is natural to inquire into the evidences of the retention of this ancestral habit in existing man. What abilities to lead an arboreal life are manifested in existing man ?

In such an inquiry we are liable to be led astray by many things, but none more likely to distort our outlook than the fact that modern civilized man has *learned* to climb. Schoolboys are taught to climb a rope upon lines altogether different from those employed by their Primate ancestors. A white man " shins " up a pole in a fashion foreign to the arboreal Primates; he clasps it with his knees, and with his locked legs and feet, and by approximating this hold to his hand-grasp, he clumsily and slowly progresses upwards. The European small boy climbs a tree in true monkey fashion till he comes to a branch which is nearly perpendicular, and then his only resort is to " swarm " up it. The European man has perfected his knee and leg grasp by a mechanical contrivance known to schoolboys as climbing irons, which are furnished with spikes at the points where the legs are most adopted to hugging the branch.

This method of climbing is, however, a mere adaptation to the handicap imposed by long civilization and the habit of wearing boots. It is a confession that the plastic foot-grasp is lost. Unbooted races do not " swarm " or " shin " up trees, but many of them have learned some mechanical way of assisting their waning powers of foot-grasp. One widespread method is the adoption of a hoop or girdle which encircles the tree and the man's waist, and so allows him to lean back from the trunk while his feet are firmly planted against it. This is a natural mechanical contrivance which enables the climber to use his hands for other purposes than for mere hanging on. His foot-grasp is not good enough to trust to, and an extra support is gained by the waist girdle, which allows a free use to be made of the hands for gathering fruit, incising the bark, or any other purpose.

Some races do not use the waist girdle, and they rely still more upon the foot-grasp, but supplement it by running a thong between the two big toes. This method is often made use of by Malays in climbing the almost vertical stems of coconut trees. The two feet are pressed firmly against the trunk, and the thong (about one foot long) stretching between the big toes readily adapts itself to the annular irregularities of the bark. The security afforded by this hold is very great.

But, again, other and more primitive people use no mechanical contrivance at all; they depend entirely upon a foot-grasp just as monkeys do. In some parts of the world coconuts are gathered from the trees before they are ripe enough to fall, and then very commonly, and as a matter of convenience for repeated climbing, the upright stems are notched, producing the so-called "monkey ladder." These notches will not enable an ordinary European to climb the tree in native fashion, but for the native they provide an ascent but little more difficult than the mounting of a stairway. The natives walk up these trees with great facility by taking advantage of the slight irregularities afforded by the notches.

But in other places coconuts are not gathered—they are permitted to fall when ripe, and then no monkey ladder is made upon the trees. In these places when a native climbs a tree to obtain a drinking nut, or to tap the spathe, he depends entirely upon the natural grasp which his hands and feet afford him. He does not shin or swarm up, but approximating the palms of his hands and the soles of his feet to the trunk, he walks or climbs up exactly as a monkey would under similar circumstances.

Races more primitive than the Malays can climb the perpendicular trunks of jungle trees with the greatest ease. The Sakai " can climb about like monkeys " (Skeat and Blagden) (see Fig. 79.) The Semangs, although they are not ignorant of mechanical aids, are skilful climbers in the typical manner of the Primates. " I myself once saw two of the Kedah Semang run several yards up trees by putting the flat of their feet against the trunk and their arms round it " (Skeat and Blagden). Sea-going Malays adopt the same method when climbing masts or ropes aboard ship, and in all these feats the grasp of the big toe is a very essential feature.

Tree-living habits also must not be forgotten in any review of arboreal man. Arboreal houses, or even mere arboreal leaf shelters, are well-known ethnological details of the domestic economy of some primitive races. Nor must the origin of these arboreal homes be overlooked, since their purpose is that, while the human occupants may freely climb to and fro, they are inaccessible to the more dangerous jungle beasts. The Semangs regard a shelter high up in the branches as the safest place for human babies, and they usually gain access to these houses by a slanting bamboo made purposely shiny and difficult for predatory animals to climb.

It does not matter to us how ethnologists might be disposed to regard these cases—they might label them as primitive or as degenerated—but for us they certainly show that in Man, as he is, there is an ability to climb manifested upon exactly the same lines as the climbing function of the arboreal Primates, and differing only in

14

FIG. 79.—A SAKAI TREE-CLIMBING.

From a photograph by Cerruti reproduced in "The Pagan Races
of the Malay Peninsula," by W. W. Skeat and C. O. Blagden.

that it is somewhat less perfectly performed. Modern European man has no doubt lost his foot-grasp so thoroughly that when he takes to climbing he learns a new and human method, but his less trammelled brother still conducts the business upon its primitive lines, and does it far better. Nor is the original method beyond the reach of the European, for upon the stage acrobats and animal impersonators periodically appear, possessing every feature of the typical arboreal activities of the Primates.

CHAPTER XXXI

THE FAILURES OF ARBOREAL LIFE

THERE would seem to be a general law applicable to animal adaptations—a law which we might term *the law of successful minimal adaptive specialization.* A plastic stock, given unlimited scope of development in varied environment, tends to differentiate. Different races will specialize towards the needs of their environment. Different environments offer varying possibilities of education, expansion, and advance, but the full educational possibilities are not necessarily grasped solely, or to the full, by the animal which becomes most completely specialized. This is a fact made clear by a whole sequence of geological types which have seized upon their environmental opportunities, and have become specialized in an extraordinary degree to fit their environment, only to arrive at specific senility, and be supplanted by less specialized and more plastic types. A complete, early, and all-absorbing specialization is almost synonymous with specific senility. An animal which specializes to the limits, in response to its environment, becomes a slave to its environment, and loses its greatest evolutionary asset of plasticity. This, in the end, spells the doom of progress. It does not matter greatly in what venture the all-absorbing specialization is cultivated. It may be in response to environment; it may be in protective mechanisms, it may be in diet. As Willey has said, " Hardly anything proclaims a finished organization, the culmination of a phyletic career, so plainly as an exclusive diet."

A specialization for blood-sucking, a specialization for

eating ants, or an adaptation for any other very definite and special type of food, has proved the downfall of many a promising animal type.   The Primate and human stock has not been led astray in this direction; for it has preserved throughout that well-balanced habit of dietary, only to be termed omnivorous.   To talk in the fashion of human successes in life, an animal may use or abuse its life surroundings.   We may say that when it uses them rightly it undergoes the *successful minimal adaptive specialization*, but when it abuses them it runs riot in specializations—specializations which ultimately make it the slave of its environment.

An animal which chances to come into possession of a habitat of which one feature is the presence of water— be it rivers, lakes, or oceans—in which food is to be obtained will open up a wider field for its activities, gain a new series of educational possibilities, and perhaps place itself beyond the competition of a rival by acquiring, in some degree, an aquatic habit.   To be at home both upon the land and in the water offers a wider field under normal circumstances, and a useful, possibly life-saving alternative under abnormal circumstances, that is an obvious asset to the animal.   But to go much further than this in the cultivation of an aquatic habit is to court disaster, since a purely aquatic life is one singularly barren of educational possibilities.   Limbs become reduced to paddles; smell, hearing, and even sight, become restricted senses, and an animal wholly dependent on a thoroughly aquatic life is one debarred from real mammalian progress.   The *Sirenia*, *Cetacea* (toothed and toothless) and even the *Pinnipeda* among the Mammals, are examples of types which, having become slaves of an aquatic habit, and leading singularly restricted, though highly specialized lives, have fallen behind in the march of progress.   It is notorious how long in geological history these animals have been, as it were, finished organisms.

The same story could be told of every condition of distinctive environment. Some animals have acquired a highly useful power of burrowing in the earth for the purpose of making safe retreats for themselves and their young, or for obtaining food below the surface of the earth; some animals have become highly specialized slaves to this habit. The Insectivorous Moles (*Talpidœ*), the Golden Moles (*Chrysochloridœ*), the Rodent Mole Rats (*Spalacidœ*), and the marsupial *Notoryctes*, are examples of highly specialized failures in this direction.

It is not likely that a habitat so attractive and so universally present as the tree-tops would fail to be abused by some members of the stocks which have taken possession of it. It is the distinction of the human stock —a distinction to which we have had frequent occasion to allude—that it never became the slave of its arboreal environment, for it became adapted to tree life in a strictly tempered manner, and it specialized to the successful minimum degree.

It will be best to note the particular specializations which arboreal animals are likely to develop to such an extent as to imperil their future evolutionary progress. First are those special adaptations for clinging tight to branches, securing for the animal a high degree of arboreal safety at the initial expense of some of its activity. The more the clinging adaptations are developed the more hampered become the real climbing powers, and the less the chance of producing a truly emancipated fore-limb. All four climbing limbs become clinging limbs, the grasping hands and feet become alike mere claw-like adaptations of the members to the branches, and even claws and nails may turn into hooks.

Phascolarctus, among the Metatheria, is a mere arboreal clinger with activities greatly reduced, and its educational possibilities almost gone. It possesses an opposable big toe, but its hand has undergone a change reminiscent of ventures seen in avian and reptilian orders, for the thumb and first finger are opposed to the other three digits. The eutherian Sloths (*Bradypodidæ*) show to perfection the fatal effects of mere arboreal clinging. These animals spend their lives for the most part among the branches of trees, to which they cling hooked up in an inverted position by a reduced and highly specialized series of digits. The educational possibilities that the arboreal habit offers to a Sloth are extremely limited; even the range of its diet becomes restricted, and an animal that has become an arboreal clinger is an animal entering upon specific senility. With the phylogenetic history, and the affinities of the *Bradypodidæ* we are not here concerned, but perhaps they are not beyond the suspicion of having certain Primate linkages, and it would be easy to point the moral of the tendency to such a sloth-like condition already manifested in *Nycticebus tardigradus*. This Lemur may easily be appealed to as an example of a tendency to arboreal clinging which may possibly be exaggerated, and so lead astray from the line of true Primate development. *Nycticebus* may also be pointed to as showing possible tendencies to two other outcomes of the arboreal habit which prove pitfalls of specialization in arboreal animals. We have noticed the tendency shown by this animal to trust to the suspending grasp of its feet rather than to that of its hands; it frequently turns upside down, and hangs head downwards. This is apparently a somewhat similar manifestation of tho trust to foot-grasp which has become so highly elaborated in some New World Monkeys. It is a strange feature of the South American arboreal animals that they have assisted and perfected the foot-grasp by the development of a prehensile tail. It might seem that the acquirement of this new grasping organ, with all its beautiful motor and sensory adaptations, would be a distinct advance in the evolution of the Primates. Yet it has proved to be a specialization which turned aside its possessors from real progress.

The South American monkeys are sometimes named "four-handed," but some of them might, with equal justice, be termed five-handed, so perfect is the specialization of the tail for all grasping and tactile functions. Yet in this multiplicity of hands there is no evolutionary gain. The true hands lose some of their perfections in this sharing of their duties by other members, and the animal becomes so much a perfected arboreal acrobat, that advances in any other direction are wellnigh impossible.

With the other specialized results of arboreal habit it is less easy to deal. That flying Mammals have originated from arboreal Mammals is certain. The Indo-Malayan and Australasian faunas teem with the representatives of several orders which, having become thoroughly arboreal, have gained some powers of aerial flight. The particular arboreal specialization which culminated in the power of flight is difficult to determine with certainty, since comparative anatomy helps but little, and paleontology not at all. There are, for instance, no geological evidences of the types which linked the Bats (already fully perfected in Eocene times) with any other mammalian order from which they were derived. The curious Flying Lemur *Galeopithecus volans* (see Fig. 80) has been regarded by many anatomists as an existing remnant of such a link, and *Cheiromeles torquatus*, a Bornean Bat, possesses many of the characters of a true tree-climber (see Fig. 81). But these creatures hardly tell us how the habit of flight was acquired as an arboreal specialization. It is natural to assume that an arboreal animal which has learned to leap from branch to branch in the astonishing manner evinced by many of the Lemurs should progress in its special line by launching itself into the air and increasing the lengths in its leaps by gliding, or planing, on an outstretched membrane derived from some part of its anatomy. There are many leaping aerial gliders: we may instance the marsupial

Flying Phalanges (*Petaurus, Acrobates*, etc.) and the rodent Flying Squirrels (*Pteromys, Anomalurus*, etc.) which have made some progress towards flight. But it

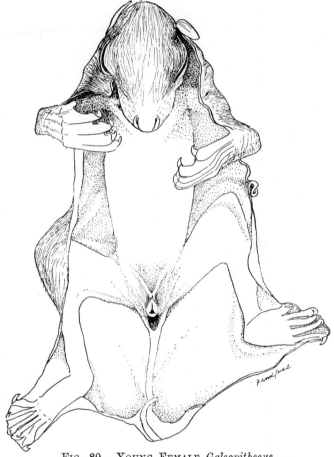

Fig. 80.—Young Female *Galeopithecus*.
From a specimen collected by Charles Hose.

is to be doubted if the truly flying Mammals, such as the Bats, started their career on these lines.

According to Willey, " the facts seem to show clearly that it is not merely the habit of taking flying leaps, like

Fig. 81.—The Naked Bat (*Cheiromeles torqua'us*) which shows, particularly in the Structure of its Hind-Limbs, Adaptations to a Tree-climbing Habit.

From a spirit specimen collected by Dr. Charles Hose, Sarawak, Borneo.

monkeys, for example, that has led to the formation of organs of flight." Certainly there is nothing in the anatomy of *Cheiromeles* or of *Galeopithecus* to indicate any inheritance of a power of arboreal leaping. Assuming that the Bats are monophylic and that *Cheiromeles* might show an evolutionary phase representative of the fore-runners of all the members of the order (an assumption I believe to be by no means justified), one might be inclined to imagine that the specialization of foot-grasping and the consequent adaptation of an inverted position, such as we have noted in *Nycticebus*, was an early phase of the evolution of true mammalian flight. It is of interest to remark here that more than one existing Lemur shows a definite development of a lateral skin fold such as constitutes, when fully developed, a flying membrane or patagium. Beddard has called attention to such a rudiment in *Propithecus*, and more recently Anthony and Bortnowsky have described a pleuropatagium in *Microcebus (cheirogaleus) minor* under the name of " un appareil aérien de type particulier."

We will not probe the origin of mammalian flight any further, nor turn aside to inquire if all the flying Mammals grouped as the *Cheiroptera*, or Bats, have sprung at the same time, and in the same manner, from the arboreal mammalian stem; we will be content to see to what ends this new acquisition led. At first sight, it would seem that the ability to fly would be an enormous asset to a Mammal already passed through the apprenticeship of arboreal life. A flying animal knows no limits of habitat or environment; geographical barriers, which limit the activity and spread of the stock from which it sprang, offer no unsurmountable boundaries to its enterprises. Indeed, the geographical distribution of the *Cheiroptera* demonstrates the reality of this advantage.

The power of flight, whilst offering an abundant change of habitat, affords also an almost unlimited range of dietary; it facilitates escape from enemies, and provides a ready means of avoiding local overcrowding, rivalry, or temporary local adversity. All these things are assets —enormous assets—in the preservation and multiplication of the type; and the specific richness, the enormous numbers of individuals, and wide-world distribution of the Bats, are evidence of this. But it must be remembered that, despite the undoubted successes of the flying Mammals in these limited directions, there has been an evolutionary stasis in the group extending over a very long geological period. They have obviously gained their freedom, and their specific plasticity at the expense of some very vital evolutionary asset. The thing which they have lost in taking to an aerial life is the very thing which they won in their arboreal life, the factor which made their aerial enterprises possible—the emancipation of the fore-limb. Their fore-limbs have become purely specialized as " wings " ; they are no longer useful for grasping, for touch, for examination and for all the other functions which we have seen are so essential in the final education of the neopallium which makes for real evolutionary progress. No matter from what sources, and by what routes, the whole of the flying Mammals comprised within the limits of the order *Cheiroptera* were derived, we may regard them all as animals which, having sacrificed the very valuable freedom of the fore-limb to the powers of flight, had flourished exceedingly as a consequence of their enterprise, but had progressed but little in real evolution, since the very factor which enabled them to take their momentous step had been altogether absorbed in taking the step.

CHAPTER XXXII

THE UPRIGHT POSTURE

It will be gathered from a perusal of the foregoing
chapters that, in the main, I have attempted to derive
most of the peculiar features of Man, and of his kindred,
from adaptations and advantages gained during an
arboreal apprenticeship. To this source of derivation of
these adaptations I can see no real alternative; but it
must be pointed out that most of the physical details
to which I have called attention are generally explained
as being outcomes of the "attainment of the erect
posture." The problem of making Man has, indeed,
commonly been regarded as " the turning of an ordinary
quadruped a quarter of a circle into the vertical plane "
(Robert Munro). There is here evinced that unnatural
and thoroughly mechanical picture of " the far-reaching
effects on the organism of this slow and painful acquisition
of a radically new posture " at which Dwight and some
few others, have scoffed, but which underlies so tena-
ciously much modern anthropological teaching. The
erect position of Man is obvious, but I heartily agree with
Dwight when he says that " as an explanation it has been
terribly overworked." Walking upright upon the surface
of the earth has produced its changes in the human body,
of this there is no doubt; but we must be careful to distinguish between these " finishing touches " and those
other changes which are so much older and so much
more important—the adaptations to arboreal life.

We may not say at what point in the evolutionary
story the rising member of this stock became what all

would agree to name as a human being. We have now a complexity of species, and even genera, of "human" remains, and yet, as is indeed inevitable, we have no criterion by which all will agree to judge such remains as belonging to an evolutionary stage universally recognized as being "human." Some, it is true, have boldly taken this question in hand—or, rather, have made assertions as to when the change took place, and when the ancestor of Man became definitely human.

Munro has stated his conviction clearly, and, for him, *Homo sapiens* came into being with the "attainment of the erect position," and the consequent possession of its accompanying benefits. But the statement of his case needs examination: "With the attainment of the erect position and the consequent specialization of his limbs into hands and feet, Man entered on a new phase of existence. With the advantage of manipulative organs and progressive brain he became *Homo sapiens*."

If it be these things which determine *Homo sapiens* as a species, then *Homo sapiens* need not be limited to Man the upright, for all these things are effects of an arboreal life, and we know not to what lengths they had carried evolution while the animal was still arboreal. Even if we are to limit our ideas of "Man" to an animal which walks upright upon its two feet, we must not fall into the very usual error of ascribing to this upright posture all those changes and benefits accumulated among the branches. Different anatomists have assigned varying importance to the upright posture, and its accompanying blessings. Among the earlier of them it was customary to see something very distinctive—typically human, if not partially divine—in this posture. "In the external conformation of man we immediately remark his upright stature; that majestic attitude which announces his superiority over all the other inhabitants of the globe." This is the statement of William Lawrence, a man who in 1820 was regarded by the authorities of St. Bartho-

lemew's as a very dangerous and unorthodox thinker
and teacher concerning the zoological status of Man.
It is certainly not so enthusiastically eulogistic as are the
statements of almost all who went before, and many
who came after him. In 1862 John Goodsir chose as
the subject for his summer session lectures, " The Dignity
of the Human Body." It is easy to picture the circumstances under which these lectures were given to the
students of Edinburgh University; it is easy to understand
the enthusiasm which Goodsir put into their composition;
but it is extremely difficult to realize how the fascination
of such a subject could lead so competent an anatomist
to pen some of the extraordinary nonsense contained in
these lectures. It would be easy to furnish a long list
of quotations from the works of modern anthropologists
to show the enormous importance commonly assigned to
this matter of standing and walking upright. It would
be equally easy to show that, in most cases, the changes
which they are picturing as being produced by it are in
reality due to the much older climbing activities of the
animal. It is far more difficult to find any written word
of dissent from such views.

Nevertheless Dwight made his position clear when he
wrote: " The upright position is certainly one of the
great human characteristics, but I am not carried away
by the enthusiasm with which some authors dilate on it."
Elliot Smith alludes to " the common fallacy of supposing
that the erect attitude is Man's distinctive prerogative,
and of regarding the assumption of that position and
mode of progression as the determining factor in the
evolution of Man." Klaatsch has asserted, with more
directness, that " Man and his ancestors were never
quadrupeds as the dog, or the elephant, or the horse."

With this plain statement it is quite impossible to disagree, when one studies the condition of the bones and
muscles of the human fore-limb. Right from that dawn
period in which the Therapsida of the Triassic gave birth

to the ancestors of the Mammals, the fore-limb of the mammalian stock from which Man sprang has been spared from the servile function of merely supporting the body weight in quadrupedal progression. "Man and his ancestors were never quadrupeds;" there has never been "a slow and painful acquisition of a radically new position." Until Man walked upon the earth in "that majestic attitude which announces his superiority over all the other inhabitants of the globe," he and his forebears climbed and walked about the branches of the trees.

No "ordinary quadruped" was turned through "a quarter of a circle into the vertical plane." But some extremely primitive Mammal climbed a tree, lived and evolved among its branches, and after long ages walked to earth again as that Primate destined to be the dominant member of the animal kingdom. That the upright habit is of the very first importance as an evolutionary factor and as a human possession must be freely admitted. But that this upright habit is the distinct prerogative of Man is a proposition not to be entertained for a moment.

That there is an alternative to the all too common idea that a four-footed pronograde Mammal must have become upright in process of the making of mankind is, I think, obvious. And that this alternative is the gradual readjustment incidental to an arboreal life, I conceive to be certain. The human child sits up before it stands; the human stock sat up before it stood.

BIBLIOGRAPHY

Bell, Sir Charles.
The Hand, its Mechanism and Vital Endowments as evincing Design. Bridgwater Treatise No. IV. London, 1833.

Blagden, C. O.
See **Skeat.**

Bolton, Joseph Shaw.
The Functions of the Frontal Lobes. *Brain*, 1903, p. 215.

Bonney, Victor.
See **Taylor.**

Darwin, Charles.
The Descent of Man. First edition. London, 1871.

Duckworth, W. L. H.
Morphology and Anthropology. Cambridge, 1904, and New Edition of vol. i., 1915.

Dwight, Thomas.
Thoughts of a Catholic Anatomist. London, 1911.

Elliot Smith, G.
The Origin of Mammals. Discussion, Section D. British Association, 1911.
Presidential Address. Section H. British Association, 1912.
Arris and Gale Lectures on "The Evolution of the Brain." *Lancet*, 1910, p. 153.

Ellis, Thomas S.
The Human Foot, its Form and Structure, Functions and Clothing London, 1889.

Forbes, Henry O.
A Handbook of the Primates. Two vols. London, 1896.

Gadow, Hans.
Observations in Comparative Myology. *Journ. Anat. and Phys.* vol. xvi., p. 493.

Goodsir, John.
Anatomical Memoirs. Edited by William Turner. 1868.

Hartman, Robert.
Anthropoid Apes. Second edition. London, 1889.

Hickson, Sydney J.
A Naturalist in North Celabes. London, 1889.

Humphry, Sir G. M.
Observations in Myology. London, 1872.
The Human Foot and the Human Hand. London, 1861.
See also Journ. Anat. and Phys., vol. iii., p. 320, and vol. vi., p. 1.

Huntington, G. S.
Numerous Studies in Myology. See especially *American Journal of Anatomy*, vol. ii., No. 2, p. 157.

Huxley, Thomas Henry.
Evidence as to Man's Place in Nature. Third thousand. London, 1864.

Keith, Arthur.
Introduction to the Study of Anthropoid Apes. London, 1897.
On the Chimpanzees and their Relationship to the Gorilla. *Proc Zool. Soc.*, 1899, p. 296.
Hunterian Lectures on "Certain Phases in the Evolution of Man." *Brit. Med. Journ.*, 1912, pp. 734 and 788.

Kidd, Dudley.
Savage Childhood, a Study of Kafir Children. London, 1906.

Kloster, Rudolph.
On the M. Pronator Radii Teres of the Mammals. *Anatomische Hefte*, 1901, p. 671.

Lawrence, Sir William.
Lectures on the Comparative Anatomy, Physiology, Zoology, and the Natural History of Man. Ninth edition. London, 1844.

Macalister, Alex.
On the Arrangement of the Pronator Muscles in the Limbs of Vertebrate Animals. *Journ. Anat. and Phys.*, vol. iii., p. 335.

Munro, Robert.
Presidential Address. Anthropological Section, British Association, 1893.

Parsons, F. G.
Numerous Studies in Myology. See especially *Journ. Anat. and Phys.*, vol. xxxii., p. 428, etc.

Sclater, W. L. and P. L.
The Geography of Mammals. London, 1899.

Skeat, W. W., and Blagden, C. O.
Pagan Races of the Malay Peninsula. London, 1906.

Taylor, Gordon, and Bonney, Victor.
Homology and Morphology of the Popliteus Muscle. *Journ. Anat. and Phys.*, vol. xl., p. 34.

Topinard, Paul.
Anthropology. English edition, 1890.

Wallace, A. R.
The Malay Archipelago.

Willey, Arthur.
Convergence in Evolution. London, 1911.

INDEX

A

ACCESSORY muscles of respiration, 135
Adaptation to environment, 3
Aerial life, 216
American monkeys, 69, 215
Amphibia, 16, 20
Anchoring nipples, 144
Anous stolidus, nesting of, 201
Anthony, Professor Raoul, 219
Anticlinal vertebra, 103
Aquatic animals, 56, 213
Arctomys, 85
Archepallium, 151
Ariens Kappers, Dr., 163
Association areas, 191
Association of senses, 178
Auditory impressions, 174

B

Baboon, skull of, 116
  pelvis of, 125
Balancing muscles, 65
Bambute Pygmies, limbs of, 202
Bats, hind-limb of, 55
  pelvis of, 127
  mammary glands of, 143
  as failures, 217
Beddard on lemurs, 219
Bell, Sir Charles, on the hand, 43
  on respiration, 134
Big toe, grasping power of, 72
Binocular vision, 176
Birds, feet of, 67
Boots, wearing out, 205
Bradypodidæ, 215
Brain, evolution of, 194
  importance in evolution, 200
Bridgwater treatise, 43
Broom on limbs, 11
Burrowing animals, 214

C

Canine teeth, 90
Carotid arteries, 96
Carpus, 23
Cat washing face, 19
Centetes, litter of, 139
  mammary glands of, 141

Centre of motion, 104
Cercopithecus, vertebral column of, 120
Cerebral hemispheres, 150
Chameleon, feet of, 67
Cheirogaleus, 138
Cheiromeles, 216
Cheiropods, 197
Chelonians, 20, 40
Chest, shape of, 131
Chimpanzee, 37, 112, 126, 187, 202
Chin a human feature, 95
Chiromys, 154
Chrysochloris, 59
Clavicle, 28
Climbing, dawn of, 16
Coconuts, method of gathering, 208
Conduct, evolution of, 181
  conception of, 193
Conscience, 194
Convergent mimics, 197
Corpus callosum, 198
  striatum, 171
Cortex, development of, 150
  method of building of, 164
Crocidura, 39
Crocodile, vertebral column of, 102
Cryptobranchus, 33, 58
Curves of spine, 119
Cynocephalus, 116
Cynodontia, 149

D

Darwin, 1, 3, 90
Decapitation of bird, 169
Dental caries, 93
Dentine, 94
Descartes, 194
Descending trees, methods of, 50
De Vries, 3
Diaphragm, 133
Diet, specialization in, 212
Digital formula, 75
Dipnoi, brain of, 150
Dog, 19, 167, 175
Duckworth, Dr. W. L. H., 81, 91, 202
Dwight, Professor Thomas, 2, 180, 221

227